NEW BIO

28

NEW BIOLOGY

EDITED BY

M. L. JOHNSON

MICHAEL ABERCROMBIE

G. E. FOGG

28

PENGUIN BOOKS

Penguin Books Ltd, Harmondsworth, Middlesex
U.S.A.: Penguin Books Inc., 3300 Clipper Mill Road, Baltimore 11, Md
AUSTRALIA: Penguin Books Pty Ltd, 762 Whitehorse Road, Mitcham, Victoria

—

Published January 1959
Copyright © Penguin Books Ltd, 1959

—

Made and printed in Great Britain by
The Campfield Press, St Albans

During 1959 there will be three issues of *New Biology*, appearing in January, May, and October. Subscriptions are accepted at 11/- for four issues, post free. Of the previous issues, Numbers 2–4 and 12–27 inclusive are still available. If there is any difficulty in obtaining any of these from a bookseller they may be had by writing direct to the publisher

CONTENTS

THE VOYAGE OF THE BEAGLE

P. D. F. MURRAY

It is likely that the voyage of the *Beagle* round the world, from the end of 1831 to October 1836, will be famous among the great journeys of the world, so long as our scientific civilization endures. Its fame depends on no great geographical discovery, for it revealed no new continent or even island, and on no great feat of heroism or endurance, but on the work of one man who travelled on the ship, made observations and accepted into his mind ideas which, much later, like slowly germinating seeds, were to flower into a great theory worthy to stand, among the greatest achievements of the human mind, beside the heliocentric solar system of Copernicus and Galileo, the gravitation of Newton, and the atomism of Democritus, Dalton, and Rutherford. The man, of course, was Charles Darwin, and the theory that of evolution, which Darwin did not originate, but which he made irresistible to the unbiased mind.

It would be quite impossible, within the space available, to give any idea of the content of Darwin's book on the voyage. If Darwin had never written anything else, it would stand worthily beside other great travel books of the nineteenth century, such as Bates' *Travels on the Amazons.* To find this out, the book itself must be read, and not articles about the book. A single article can do no more than to pick out some particular subject which the book treats, or some particular aspect of the treatment. For the history of science, the interest of *The Voyage of the* Beagle lies in the evidence it contains of the reception into its author's mind of observations which would later be brought to bear on the Theory of Evolution, and of their effect on that mind, in leading it to those thoughts which later, in the *Origin of Species*, transformed the biological sciences, and had their repercussions in every other field of intellectual effort.

When H.M.S. *Beagle* sailed from Devonport on 27 December 1831, Darwin was a young man of nearly twenty-three. He had just come down from Cambridge, where he was supposed to have been studying theology in preparation for entry into the Ministry of the Church of England; but he does not seem to have studied theology with any great enthusiasm and he had entered upon these studies only after an unsuccessful attempt at medical studies at Edinburgh. His real enthusiasm was for natural history, a term which covered wide interests in zoology, botany, and geology. Professor Henslow, a distinguished botanist, had been a friend of Darwin at Cambridge, and it was through him that, when the *Beagle* expedition was decided upon, the Lords of the Admiralty offered to young Mr Darwin the position of Naturalist with her complement. It was clear to Mr Darwin's family that this change of occupation was not likely greatly to advance his progress in the Ministry of the Church of England, and the change was not welcome at home; nevertheless, Charles Darwin went on the voyage.

At that time, it must have seemed that science had shown a picture of the world and the universe which was destined to last. The heliocentric solar system was secure, the sun and the planets had condensed and cooled from clouds of incandescent gas; and the modern theory of concretion had not yet been put forward; astronomy was founded on gravitation, Einstein was far in the future, and chemistry sat firmly on its unbroken atom. In geology, Lyell's *Principles* had been published in 1830 and 1832, completing the second phase of the great scientific revolution that Copernicus and Galileo had begun. It was now established beyond doubt that the Earth was enormously older than the few thousand years allowed it by traditional Jewish and Christian belief; a reasonable modern figure is 3,000–4,000 million years. It was also established that while there had been catastrophes and to spare in the history of the world, it was not the catastrophic changes, the earthquakes and volcanoes, which had been important in moulding the surface of the world, but the little quiet, day-to-day changes, erosion by the rain and the wind, and the slow, imperceptible raising and depressing of lands and mountain chains. This was important for the following reason. That fossils exist had long been known and that they were the real remains of real animals and plants was no longer doubted, but very few had yet seriously questioned the literal truth of the account of Creation as given in the Book of Genesis, and so, somehow, Genesis and the fossils had to be made to fit. This was achieved by imagining a series of separate and distinct creations, each fauna and flora destroyed by a catastrophe, and a new one created when the catastrophe was over. The new geology flatly rejected this theory of world evolution by catastrophe. In the biological sciences, the existence of distinct species had always been recognized and, while Genesis remained unchallenged, there could be no problem about their origin: they had all been instantaneously created, and had remained unchanged ever since. We have Darwin's own word for it that when he set out in the *Beagle* it had not occurred to him to doubt the literal truth of Genesis; but certainly there are several passages in the book which show that things he saw on the voyage did awake in his mind the thought that the origin of species was, to use his own words, a 'mystery'. It is hard to see how there could be a mystery unless there was a doubt.

Darwin then, as he went on the *Beagle*, was a young man with this background, and to the background he added a wide and apparently untiring interest, great powers of observation, and a mind which, seeking causes, effects, relationships, comparisons, and contrasts, was always asking 'why'. I think it is the extraordinary width of Darwin's interests which strike one most when reading the book, and yet there are curious gaps. Anything zoological, geological, or botanical, excites his interest, but he seems much more interested in things on land than in the sea. There is much about human affairs on land, about individuals and classes of men, like the Gauchos of Brazil, and about human institutions, such as the slavery then existing in South America as also in the Southern States of the North; but there is very little about the *Beagle* herself or, except for cordially expressed thanks to Captain Fitzroy, her commander, and to her other officers, anything about the personalities with whom Darwin was so closely associated. There is also very little about himself. Indeed, the book is far from being a personal narrative. At the end of the book, one knows that Darwin was a very able naturalist, one knows that he went here and went there, saw this and saw that, and devised such and such theories, but apart from a few references to ill health, beyond this one has no clue at all to what manner of man Mr Darwin may have been. The reason I imagine to be simple enough. Darwin was always a humble man, who thought people would be interested in the animals and plants and rocks of the lands he visited, but to whom it never occurred that they might perhaps be interested in himself.

The purpose of the *Beagle*'s voyage was to survey the coast of Patagonia and Tierra del Fuego, Chile, Peru, and some Pacific Islands, 'and to carry a chain of chronometrical measurements round the world'.

Leaving Devonport, they went to the Cape de Verde Islands, thence to St Paul's Rocks, a small group of sea bird covered rocks in the middle of the Atlantic. Here Darwin began that interest in islands which reached its climax in the Galápagos, finding at St Paul's Rocks no vegetation and but two species of sea bird – a noddy and a tern, and several insects and spiders – a fly and a tick which live on the birds, a small moth believed to feed on feathers, a beetle and a wood-louse from beneath the dung of the birds, and numerous spiders which presumably prey on the insects. Next, after a call at another island, the *Beagle* went on to Bahia, in San Salvador, on the coast of Brazil, and thence further south to Rio de Janeiro. Here Darwin made the first of a series of long overland journeys which enabled him to observe so much of the lands he was visiting.

His account of Rio is in his second chapter, and I do not think one can better give an idea of the general character of the book than by mentioning briefly the subjects with which it deals. Beginning the overland journey just mentioned, he writes of large and brilliant butterflies, and in the same paragraph relates the story of some runaway slaves whose stronghold had been in a hill which the party crossed; discovered, the slaves were captured by a party of soldiers, all but one old woman who 'dashed herself to pieces from the summit of the mountain. In a Roman matron this would have been called the noble love of freedom; in a poor negress it is mere brutal obstinacy.' Darwin was a humane man, and there is much more in this chapter about slavery, in which the cruelty of man is related with indignation, and the conjunction, in the same individual, of callousness to slaves with humanity and good feeling in other directions, is recounted with astonishment.

A little later in the chapter, Darwin mentions planarian worms, simply organized terrestrial and fresh water worms, of which in the Southern Hemisphere he collected twelve species, including some from Van Diemen's Land. Some of these he kept alive and, cutting them in half, observed their remarkable powers of regeneration.

Next comes a description of a hunting expedition with a Portuguese priest, and this leads to comments on the Brazilian habit of carrying knives and throwing them, and the resulting frequency of murders.

This is followed by observation on the behaviour of clouds, and on the local climate, and thence via certain frogs and insects to fire-flies; upon these latter Darwin performed several simple experiments. Through all his life, Darwin experimented, always with great ingenuity and very simple equipment.

Next comes a description of the jumping of a luminous beetle, then a brief description of the Botanical Gardens at Rio, of the flight of humming birds, of more butterflies and beetles, of the army ants and their destruction of their prey, and of spiders, and the chapter closes. It is an exceptional chapter in one respect: there is hardly any geology in it.

In Chapter III, the *Beagle* goes on, southward again to Montevideo, on the estuary of the Rio de la Plata, and the capital of Uruguay. During the next two years she was engaged in surveying the South American eastern coast, south of La Plata, and Darwin, during this time, made several overland journeys. In one of these, he became acquainted with the tucu-tuco (*Ctenomys brasiliensis*), a rodent with the subterranean habits of a mole. The tucu-tuco, which apparently never comes above the ground, has little use for the sense of sight, and its eyes, though present, are often blind. Darwin had some evidence that this blindness was due rather to inflammation of the eye-lid than to any structural deficiency in the eye itself, and he expresses surprise that any animal should possess an organ frequently subject to injury. He then remarks that Lamarck would have been delighted with this fact when speculating 'probably with more truth than usual with him' upon the blindness of another subterranean rodent (*Aspalax*, probably=*Spalax*), and of *Proteus*, a blind cave-dwelling amphibian, and Darwin concluded 'no doubt Lamarck would have said that the tucu-tuco is now passing into the stage of the *Aspalax* and *Proteus*'. This passage is interesting as the first in which Darwin showed an interest in the manner in which the characters of organisms might change, and also reveals that he had read Lamarck, and had but a poor opinion of him. Nevertheless, very much later in his life Darwin accepted as a minor factor in evolutionary change, that 'inheritance of acquired characters' which Lamarck had put forward as a major factor, along with the voluntary strivings of the animal.

The next couple of chapters are about the region south from Montevideo, between Bahia Blanca and Rio Negro; Darwin travelled overland, northward, from Bahia Blanca to Buenos Aires, there rejoining the *Beagle*. At this time he collected the fossil remains of nine very large mammals, all comparatively recent forms, but all extinct. Darwin, of course, already knew about fossils, but these and many others which he studied at various times and places during the long voyage, must have impressed him with the great fact of change in the organic world. Today our vastly increased knowledge of fossils is perhaps, of all categories of evidence, that which is most convincing of evolution. Among the nine great animals whose remains Darwin found, and which were later described by the great comparative anatomist, Owen, was one called *Toxodon.* This Darwin describes as 'perhaps one of the strangest animals ever discovered'. Approaching the size of an elephant, but classified among the rodents, Darwin thought it also showed affinities with the elephants, and with the dugong and the manatee. To a modern zoologist, this would suggest evolutionary relationships between these various groups, but Darwin was content at the time to write: 'How wonderfully are the different Orders, at the present time so well separated, blended together in different points of the structure of the *Toxodon*'.

A few pages later, in discussing a small group of South American birds, he wrote: 'This small family of birds is one of those which, from its varied relations to other families, although at present offering only difficulties to the naturalist, ultimately may assist in revealing the grand scheme, common to the present and past ages, on which organized beings have been created.' Now this is not evolution, but it shows in Darwin's mind a tacit rejection of the thought that the grand scheme of creation had already been revealed in Genesis, and an anticipation that the human mind might be able to discover it by the study of natural history. It suggested, too, that Darwin was already seeing in the difficulties of the systematist – in the difficulty, that is, of classifying organisms tidily into pigeon-holes – the possibility that there might be a clue.

Almost immediately after the birds, comes a passage about a snake which combines the structure of a viper with the habits of a rattlesnake but makes its warning noise with a much simpler device. Darwin refers to this as 'a fact ... very curious and instructive, as showing how every character ... has a tendency to vary by slow degrees'. When one reads this paragraph it is impossible to be sure of Darwin's precise meaning. The words: 'Every character ... has a tendency to vary by slow degrees' express exactly what he later meant by the 'variations', which were the raw material of evolution, among which Natural Selection permitted the survival of some and not of others. But these were to be variations among the individuals of a species, and of such variation the present paragraph in *The Voyage* offers no evidence at all. He must, then, have meant variation from species to species, and from the phrase 'tendency to vary' he clearly meant not differences between species taken as given, but something much more dynamic, something close to 'differences occurring, whereby species change'. He must, in writing this chapter, have been very close to evolution; but the liberating idea of Natural Selection was still lacking.

It must be remembered that Darwin was at least as much a geologist as a biologist, and that geological studies occupy a great part of the *Voyage*; I am giving little time to them partly from ignorance of geology, but partly because they did not lead to any such revolution in geological theory as his zoological and botanical studies did, eventually, in biology. But the study of great mammalian fossils was thus united with a study of the geological history of the Pampas, and also with an interesting discussion of the sort of vegetation which must have been needed to support these great brutes. Darwin disagrees with those authors who thought a much more lush flora would have been needed than that of the present arid and sterile Pampas, and points to the many large animals living in the arid plains of Africa.

In modern text-books, the geographical distribution of animals is usually given as one of the categories of evidence for evolution, and in several places in *The Voyage* Darwin turns to consideration of this subject. Thus, in Chapter VII, which describes a journey from Buenos Aires to the inland town of Santa Fe, he finds more large fossil mammals, and comments upon the existence in South America, thus revealed, of a Mastodon, possibly of another elephant, of a hollow-horned ruminant and of a horse, all creatures known to have existed in North America. Today, the faunas of North and South America are very different, but formerly were much more alike. North America had hollow-horned ruminants, elephants, mastodons, horses, and the three big ground sloths: *Mega-*

therium, which was bigger than an elephant, *Megalonyx*, and *Mylodon*, the smallest of the three, only the size of an ox; South America had mastodon, horse, hollow-horned ruminants, and the same three ground sloths. Darwin interprets the earlier zoological resemblance between the two Americas in terms of migration of mammals from Asia across dry land where now is Behring Straits, and a subsequent extinction of many forms in South America and, presumably, in North America too. Again there is no evolution in all this, but there is a naturalistic interpretation of the fact observed. Certain animals at least are where they are because they have migrated there, not because they were created there at the beginning. Presumably Darwin still regarded indigenous forms as having been locally created.

After this passage, the book contains nothing further to suggest that evolutionary ideas might have been fermenting in the author's mind, until there comes a casual remark in Chapter VIII, in which he describes how a Gaucho forced a restive horse to swim a river; the process involves the man's stripping off his clothes, and Darwin remarks: 'A naked man on a naked horse is a fine spectacle; I had no idea how the two animals suited each other.' I perhaps overstate my case, but it seems to me that readiness to refer to a man as an animal indicates a mind which might be willing to accept the idea of a physical relationship of Man with the animal kingdom.

The *Beagle* went south again, to Patagonia, and there is much in the book about the geology of that province of Argentine. At Port St Julia, which is towards the south of Patagonia, Darwin found half the fossilized skeleton of yet another great mammal, *Macrauchenia patochonica*, which was as big as a camel and extinct only in the Pleistocene. This starts him off on one of the most interesting disquisitions in the entire book. He was struck by the fact that the fossil animals found in fairly recent deposits in South America belong to the same, or to related groups, as those found living today, and he wrote: 'The relationship, though distant, between the *Macrauchenia* and the Guanaco, between the *Toxo-*

don and the Capybara – the closer relationship between the many extinct Edenata and the living sloths, ant-eaters and armadillos, now so eminently characteristic of South American zoology – and the still closer relationship between the fossil and living species of *Ctenomys* and *Hydrochaerus*, are most interesting facts. This relationship is shown wonderfully – as wonderfully as between the fossil and extinct Marsupial animals of Australia – by the great collection lately brought to Europe from the caves of Brazil by MM. Lund and Clausen. In this collection there are extinct species of all the thirty-two genera, excepting four, of the terrestrial quadrupeds now inhabiting the provinces in which caves occur; and the extinct species are much more numerous than those now living; there are fossil ant-eaters, armadilloes, tapirs, peccaries, guanacos, opossums, and numerous South American gnawers and monkeys, and other animals. This wonderful relationship in the same continent between the dead and the living, will, I do not doubt, hereafter throw more light on the appearance of organic beings on our earth, and their disappearance from it, than any other class of facts.'

Nevertheless, Darwin did not in *The Voyage* take the decisive step to the hypothesis that ancient and modern forms are alike because the modern are descended from the ancient.

In the next paragraph, Darwin remarks that America must formerly have swarmed with great monsters, where now we find mere pygmies, and he proceeds to a discussion of the extinction of animals. In the course of this, he says quite casually that 'the tendency in every animal to increase by propagation is geometrical', yet that the numbers of individuals rarely so multiply, therefore 'that some check is constantly preventing the too rapid increase of every organized being left in a state of nature', but that we scarcely ever know the nature of the check or when, in the life history of the animal, it acts. This is practically a demand for the modern science of Population Ecology, whose central problem this is; but it is even more than this, for the failure of animals to multiply geometrically in spite of their geometrical rate of propagation was later to be a thought basic to the concept of Evolution by Natural Selection. The idea of Selection was still missing and would not enter Darwin's mind for long years yet to come, but we have seen, in connexion with the snake, how close he must have been to the concept of variation. This quite fascinating passage concludes with a paragraph which is puzzling to the modern reader, for it argues that the natural consequence of increasing rarity in a species is its extinction, and to us this seems obvious beyond the need of argument. The explanation must lie in the Theory of Catastrophism, which called in such extraordinary agents as terrestrial convulsions to destroy whole faunas that there might be room for the creation of another. Darwin argues that many species are, in fact, rare, and that to call in such agents to account for their extinction is not more logical than to suppose, when a sick man dies, that he died by violence.

For a long time, this is the last passage of evolutionary interest. The *Beagle* went on to Santa Cruz, also in Patagonia, and to the Falkland Islands, lying far down in the South Atlantic. There is more Patagonian geology, an interesting section on Condors, including experiments on their sense of smell and observations on their soaring flight, and on the geology and natural history of the Falkland Islands. In connexion with a goose which inhabits those islands, and which is flightless but uses its wings to beat the air, so speeding up its swimming, he mentions two other birds which use their wings otherwise than for flight – the ostrich (which uses them as sails) and the penguin; but there is no suggestion that these might be modified descendants of birds that flew. This seems odd, for we know he had read Lamarck.

Chapters X and XI are devoted to Tierra del Fuego, an archipelago of islands chopped off from the extreme end of South America, separated from it by the Straits of Magellan and ending in Cape Horn. These chapters are among the most interesting in the book, but contain little that is relevant to our present purpose. Close to the extreme southern end of Tierra del Fuego is Beagle Sound, and besides this I find in a map Mount Darwin, of which there is no mention in the book. After finally leaving those inhospitable regions, the *Beagle* was for some time in Chilean and later in Peruvian waters, and Darwin again made a number of journeys overland. These chapters do not contain much that is relevant to the development of evolutionary ideas. Such thoughts were perhaps put out of Darwin's mind, for in Chapter XIII, after mentioning some birds, he writes: 'When finding, as in this case, animals which seem to play so insignificant a part in the great scheme of nature, one is apt to wonder why they were created. But it should always be recollected that in some other country perhaps they were essential members of society, or at some former period may have been so.' This must surely be one of the most firmly orthodox statements its author ever made!

At last the *Beagle* left the South American continent, and on 15 September 1835 began the famous visit to the Galápagos Archipelago.

This archipelago, which is described in Chapter XVII, a chapter of quite exceptional interest for the history of science, consists of ten principal islands and a number of smaller ones. They lie just south of the equator, between five and six hundred miles west of the coast of South America. They are volcanic islands, and probably of geologically recent origin; they have never been united either with any other land, or with one another. They have only a small fauna and flora, but the animals and plants they do have were discovered by Darwin to be of quite exceptional interest, and to pose problems of great profundity.

To begin with, the general character of both flora and fauna is American; that is, the species present in the Galápagos Islands belong rather to American than to other groups so that, zoologically and botanically, the islands are part of the American region. Nevertheless, an extremely high proportion of both animals and plants belong to species found nowhere outside these islands, even though they may have American relatives. Thus, there were only two mammals, one a rat doubtless introduced on ships, and one a mouse, of the same genus as the house mouse, but of a special Galápagos species. Darwin knew and collected twenty-six land birds, and among these more than twenty were peculiar to the Archipelago. The indigenous forms included a hawk, two owls, a wren, three fly catchers, one dove, one swallow, and, most interesting of them all, three mocking thrushes and thirteen species of a small group of finches (the most recent figure is fourteen). The first thing, but by no means the last, which seems to have interested Darwin about these finches was that while all the species were very similar to one another (rather unexciting looking birds with black males and brown females), there were among them considerable differences in form of beak, ranging from the slender and delicate bills of some to the heavy and parrot-like beaks of others. Later work, impossible to Darwin in his brief stay at the islands, has correlated beak-form with feeding habits, and today no one doubts that the fourteen species originated from some single, or at least very few, ancestral forms which, arriving at the Galápagos from America, there differentiated into the several species, in adaptation to particular modes of life and especially (in regard to their beaks) to particular sorts of food. Darwin wrote, referring to the beaks: 'Seeing this gradation and diversity of structure in one small, intimately related group of birds, one might really fancy that from an original paucity of birds in this archipelago, one species had been taken and modified for different ends.' This is almost an evolutionary hypothesis, but with the caution which characterized all his writings, Darwin would not pass from a 'fancy' to a firm hypothesis until, many years later, he had not only accumulated vast bodies of evidence, derived from an immense variety of animals and plants, but had also a well-supported suggestion to make, as to how such changes might have been brought about. Also, the phrase 'had been taken and modified' suggests a thought of an external power in whose hands the birds were passively changed, rather than a change resulting from a set of natural circumstances.

In other groups of organisms, too, there is a similar high proportion of indigenous forms. The reptiles are few, but include the famous land tortoises found on at least the majority of the islands, and two extraordinary lizards (*Amblyrhynchus cristatus* and *A.* (now *Conolophus*) *demarlii*). All these reptiles, except the single snake, which Darwin thought might be identical with a Chilean species, are peculiar to the archipelago, and Darwin gives excellent descriptions of their general natural history. Actually a couple of small lizards are present too.

Darwin expresses surprise at the absence of toads and frogs, comments on their general absence from volcanic islands, and attributes the presence of reptiles to their possession of calcareous egg-shells which could more readily permit the eggs to be transported through the oceans. Among land molluscs were sixteen species, all but one peculiar to the Galápagos. There were few insects, mostly peculiar to the islands. Among fifteen sea fishes, all were new species and peculiar to the waters about these islands. Among 193 flowering plants, 100 were probably confined to the Archipelago.

Thus a vast majority of the land animals, and more than half of the flowering plants, though related to the animals and plants of the American region, were species confined to the Archipelago, and Darwin comments: 'It was most striking to be surrounded by new birds, new reptiles, new shells, new insects, new plants, and yet by innumerable trifling details of structure, and even by the tones of voice and plumage of the birds, to have the temperate plains of Patagonia, or the hot, dry deserts of northern Chile, vividly brought before my eyes. Why, on these small points of land, which within a late geological period must have been covered by the ocean, which are formed of basaltic lava, and therefore differ in geological character from the American continent, and which are placed under a peculiar climate – why were their aboriginal inhabitants, associated, I may add, in different proportions both in kind and number from those on the continent, and therefore acting on each other in a different manner – why were they created on American types of organization? It is probable that the islands of the Cape de Verde group resemble, in all their physical conditions, far more closely the Galápagos Islands than these latter physically resemble the coast of America; yet the aboriginal inhabitants of the two groups are totally unlike; those of the Cape de Verde

Islands bearing the impress of Africa, as the inhabitants of the Galápagos Archipelago are stamped with that of America.'

Or, in other words, if there was a creation in the Galápagos of animals and plants adapted to the Galápagos environment, why were they made similar to certain American forms? And in the Cape de Verde group, why were they similar to African forms?

The question is asked, but not answered. Instead Darwin goes on to remark that he had not as yet mentioned by far the most remarkable feature in the natural history of the archipelago: that the different islands are to a considerable extent inhabited by different but closely related species of small groups or genera, members of which are found on several or all the islands. This was first brought to his notice in regard to the tortoises, of which it seems that the different islands have different races, if not different species, but Darwin's interest in this topic was really aroused by the three species of mocking-thrushes. All those from Charles Island were of the one species, all from Albemarle Island from another, and all from James and Chatham Islands of a third species. Actually, there are four species and one of these is sub-divided into seven forms, and no island has more than one form or species (Lack, 1947).

Commenting that it is the fate of most voyagers 'no sooner to discover what is most interesting in any locality, than they are hurried from it', he regrets that most of his collection of finches from the different islands were mingled together. He did, however, obtain very strong evidence that at least some of the species of the genus *Geospiza* were confined to separate islands. In all essentials this has been amply confirmed by more recent studies, especially by Lack, but the situation is much more complex than in the case of the mocking-thrushes. Several species occupy more than one island, and many of the islands have more than one finch. Closely related finches on different islands often differ from one another, sometimes enough to justify their recognition as distinct species, sometimes only enough for them to be regarded as sub-species, unless two 'sub-species' come together on one island and, by not breeding together, reveal that they are, in fact, full species. The essential feature is the presence in groups of birds inhabiting different islands, of visibly recognizable differences in form or size or colour.

A similar situation exists in the plants; here Darwin kept the collections from the different islands separate. Four islands (James, Albemarle, Chatham, and Charles) had respectively 38, 26, 16, and 29 species limited to the Archipelago, and among these, respectively 30, 22, 12, and 21 were confined to the one island. As an example, the arborescent composite *Scalesia* may be cited. Each of its six species was limited to one island, and each to a different one. *Euphorbia*, a widely distributed genus, has eight species in the Archipelago, of which seven are confined to it, and not one found on more than one island.

Commenting, Darwin points out that the remarkable thing is, not merely that the different islands hold different species of animals and plants, but that they hold different species within small groups or genera which were common to all or most of the islands. It is the diversification, in different islands, of closely related forms, which he found so wonderful, and he writes that the only light he could throw was, that the islands were separated from one another by deep seas with currents not calculated to carry animals, plants, or seeds from one island to another, while because of a remarkable freedom from gales, the birds, insects, and seeds would not tend to be blown from island to island. He thus points to the isolation of the islands from the American mainland, and from one another, as involved presumably in preventing the mingling of the biota of different islands. But of the origin of the different species thus kept apart, he can only say: 'One is astonished at the amount of creative force, if such an expression can be used, displayed on these small, barren and rocky islands; and still more, at its diverse yet analogous action on points so near each other.' Today, of course, we attribute the diversification of the species to the isolation of their homes, which, by preventing the mingling of genes from different islands, makes possible divergent evolution in adaptation to different circumstances and modes of life, and by such diverse non-adaptive evolutionary changes as may be brought about in small isolated populations by the phenomenon of 'genetic drift'.

On leaving the Galápagos, where they seem to have spent about a month, the *Beagle* went on to Tahiti, New Zealand, New South Wales, and Tasmania (still known as Van Dieman's Land), and to Cocos Keeling, in the Indian Ocean. Problems related to the origins of species seem to have dropped out of Darwin's mind during these visits, but the chapter on Cocos Keeling (he calls it 'Keeling or Cocos') is of classical interest in both geology and biology. Many modern travellers pass, in great liners, close by this lovely atoll, and the brief moments while one sees it remain in the memory forever; but Darwin was luckier, for he remained there for ten or twelve days, and out of those ten to twelve days came Chapter XX, in which his theory of the origin of coral reefs and islands, which has stood against all criticism for well over a hundred years, was first announced. In his theory Darwin distinguished between fringing reefs, barrier reefs and atolls, regarding them as successive developmental stages, the fringing reefs forming in the shallow waters round an island, and then, as a gradual subsidence of the ocean floor lowered the island, appearing as a barrier reef separated from the island by a lagoon, and lastly as an atoll containing no central island, when the island once there had sunk beneath the waves. The most important recently proposed modification of the theory eliminates the need for a depression of the ocean floor, but accepts the same series of stages, supposing them to have been brought about by the deepening of the sea as the melting of the ice after the last glaciation added to its waters.

Leaving Cocos Keeling, the *Beagle* visited Mauritius, and then went on into the Atlantic, calling at two isolated islands in that ocean, St Helena and Ascension. At Ascension, Darwin made the last observation, related to evolutionary problems, of the voyage. There are, on this island, two varieties of rats which he thinks must have been imported, and on Ascension to 'have varied from the effect of the new conditions to which they have been exposed'; one was black and lived on the grassy summit of the island, the other was brown and lived near the settlement on the coast. It is clear that whatever Darwin may have thought, when he wrote this passage, on the mutability of species, he was quite ready to accept the formation of new varieties. Very probably he thought of these as differences induced directly by environmental circumstances. Today, we would regard such differences as without inheritable significance and (on the above assumption which, however, we would think improbable) we would not consider the two varieties of rats to be on the way to becoming distinct species. Up to this time, Darwin does not seem to have concerned himself very greatly with questions of heredity, but later he apparently thought of all variations as tending to be inherited; it must be remembered that he was writing long before Mendel. But if the differences between the varieties of rats tended to be inherited, it is hard not to believe that, somewhere in the depths of Darwin's mind, he was ready to think of them as incipient species, and, therefore, that he was ready to accept the mutability of species. When, after another brief visit to Brazil, to the Cape de Verde Islands and to the Azores, the *Beagle*, after her long voyage, came to rest at last at Falmouth, on 2 October 1836, he had still not committed himself, even to himself, to a belief that species change. But somewhere in the depths of his profound, versatile, and cautious mind, that decisive step must surely have been taken. In July of the following year he opened his first note-book on Transmutation of Species. But the joint paper with Alfred Russel Wallace: 'On the Tendency of Species to form Varieties by Natural Means of Selection' was not read before the Linnean Society of London until 1 July 1858. The 'Origin of Species' followed in 1859.

REFERENCES

Darwin, Charles. *Journal of Researches into the Geology and Natural History of the various countries visited during the voyage of H.M.S.* Beagle *round the world.* Everyman's Library edition, 1912.

Lack, David. 1947. *Darwin's Finches.* Cambridge University Press.

THE STRUCTURE OF DARWINISM

A. G. N. FLEW

THOSE who do philosophy of science tend to equate science with physics.[1] The same thing also seems often to be true of those who try to present scientific thought to non-scientists. Yet one of the most important of all scientific theories is that developed by Darwin in the *Origin of Species*.[2] Covering the entire range of biological phenomena its scope is enormous. While if any scientific theory is interesting philosophically this one is.[3] It happens also to be exceptionally suitable as an elementary example for teaching. No outlandish or elaborate concepts are involved. The nature of most of the supporting evidence is familiar, and its relevance fairly easy to grasp. The deductive moves made are short and simple. The essential material can be studied in a single original source – conveniently brief, interesting, and written well. Darwin introduces no 'theoretical entities' (photons, electro-magnetic waves, the libido, or what have you)[4] and employs no mathematics either within his theory or in presenting his case for it. The lack of these two generally essential features of modern science is at an elementary stage a positive advantage. Especially when, as here, these defects in the example may be made good afterwards by considering the later development of genetics; which both provides a hypothetical entity, the gene, and applies mathematics abundantly. The object of the present paper is not to say anything strikingly novel, but simply to suggest some of the general morals which may be drawn from an examination of this particular conceptual structure.

[1] The superscript numbers throughout the article refer to the notes at the end.

The Deductive Core of Darwinism

Darwin himself remarked in the last chapter: 'this whole volume is one long argument' (p. 413). Again in the *Autobiography*, in a typically modest and engaging passage, he claims: '*The Origin of Species* is one long argument from the beginning to the end.'[5] A recent interpreter goes further: 'The old arguments for evolution were only based on circumstantial evidence. . . . But the core of Darwin's argument was of a different kind. It did not make it more probable – it made it a certainty. Given his facts his conclusion *must* follow: like a proposition in geometry. You do not show that any two sides of a triangle are very *probably* greater than the third. You show they *must* be so. Darwin's argument was a *de*ductive one – whereas an argument based on circumstantial evidence is *in*ductive.'[6]

This is a challenging contention. For surely Darwin was a great empirical naturalist, concerned to discover what as a matter of contingent fact *is* the case, though it might not have been? What business had he with deductive *a priori* arguments purporting to demonstrate as in a theorem in geometry that some things *must* be so? We must consider what precisely this deductive core is: how much it does prove and how; and how much it leaves open to be settled by further research.

That Darwin's argument does indeed contain such a deductive core is suggested by a passage in the 'Introduction': 'As many more individuals of each species are born than can possibly survive; and as, *consequently*, there is a frequently recurring struggle for existence, *it follows that* any being, if it vary however slightly in any manner profitable to itself, under the complex and sometimes varying conditions of life will have a better chance of surviving and thus be naturally selected. From the strong principle of inheritance, any selected variety will tend to propagate its new and modified form' (p. 4: my italics). He promises that in the chapter 'Struggle for Existence' he will treat this struggle 'amongst all organic beings throughout the world, *which inevitably follows from* the high geometrical ratio of their increase' (p. 4: my italics). In that chapter he develops the argument: 'A struggle for existence *inevitably follows* from the high rate at which all organic beings tend to increase ... as more individuals are produced than can possibly survive, *there must in every case be* a struggle for existence, either one individual with another of the same species, or with the individuals of distinct species, or with the physical conditions of life. It is the doctrine of Malthus applied with manifold force to the whole animal and vegetable kingdoms, for in this case there can be no artificial increase of food, and no prudential restraint from marriage' (p. 59: my italics). Just as the struggle for existence is derived as a consequence of the combination of a geometrical ratio of increase with the finite possibilities of survival: so in the chapter 'Natural Selection' this in turn is derived as a consequence of the combination of the struggle for existence with variation. Darwin summarizes his argument here: 'If ... organic beings vary at all in the several parts of their organization, and I think this cannot be disputed; if there be ... a severe struggle for life ... and this certainly cannot be disputed; then ... I think it would be a most extraordinary fact if no variation had ever occurred useful to each being's own welfare, in the same manner as so many variations have occurred useful to man. But if variations useful to any organic being do occur, assuredly individuals thus characterized will have the best chance of being preserved in the struggle for life: and from the strong principle of inheritance they will tend to produce offspring similarly characterized. This principle of ... Natural Selection ... leads to the improvement of each creature in relation to its organic and inorganic conditions of life' (p. 115).

Since Darwin's argument does indeed contain this deductive core the pedagogic device used by Julian Huxley in his latest exposition of evolutionary theory is exceptionally apt. It can, he claims, 'be stated in the form of two general evolutionary equations. The first is that reproduction plus mutation produces natural selection; and the second that natural selection plus time produces the various degrees of biological improvement that we find in nature.'[7] The idea is excellent, but the execution here is curiously slapdash. For the first equation, as Huxley gives it ($R+M \rightarrow NS$), is not valid. Reproduction plus mutation would not necessarily lead to natural selection. It is necessary also to add the struggle for existence: and that in turn has to be derived from the sum of the geometrical ratio of increase plus the limited resources for living – limited *Lebensraum* as Hitler's Germans might have called it. So to represent the core of Darwin's argument we need something more like: $GRI+LR \rightarrow SE$; $SE+V \rightarrow NS$; and, not on all fours with the first two, $NS+T \rightarrow BI$. To avoid anachronism V (for hereditable variation) must be substituted for M (mutation). The third equation represents part of the argument which does not properly belong to what we are calling the deductive core; and so from now on we shall neglect it.

Of course to make this core, and the equations used to represent it schematically, ideally rigorous one would have to construct for all the crucial terms definitions to include explicitly every necessary assumption. There are in fact several, many of which when uncovered and noticed may seem too obvious to have been worth stating. Take for instance one to which Darwin himself refers, rather obliquely, in a passage already quoted: 'I think it would be a most extraordinary fact if no variation had ever occurred useful to each being's own welfare' (p. 115). It would indeed. He offers a very powerful reason for believing that this has not in fact been the case, adding after the phrase just quoted; 'in the same manner as so many variations have occurred useful to man' (p. 115). Nevertheless, in this particular case bringing out the assumption may have a value other than that of rigorization for its own sake. For it may suggest, what has in fact proved to be the case, that one of the main effects of natural selection is to eliminate unfavourable variations. It not only helps to generate biological improvement. It is essential to prevent biological degeneration.

We shall not attempt here to develop Darwin's argument quite rigorously or to formalize the result. This is an exercise which might be instructive. But it would of course involve transforming, and hence in a way misrepresenting, what Darwin actually said. It is perfectly possible to point the main morals without this.

(i) Though the argument itself proceeds *a priori*, because the premises are empirical it can yield conclusions which are also empirical. That living organisms all tend to reproduce themselves at a geometrical ratio of increase; that the resources they need to sustain life are limited; and that while each usually reproduces after its kind sometimes there are variations which in their turn usually reproduce after their kind: all these propositions are nonetheless contingent and empirical for being manifestly and incontestably true. That there is a struggle for existence; and that through this struggle for existence natural selection occurs: both these propositions equally are nonetheless contingent and empirical for the fact that it follows, necessarily as a matter of logic *a priori*, that wherever the first three hold the second two must hold also.

(ii) The premises are matters of obvious fact. The deductive steps are short and simple. The conclusions are enormously important. Yet these conclusions, and that they were implied by these premises, was before Darwin very far indeed from being obvious to able men already sufficiently familiar with the necessary premises. This should give us a greater respect for the power of simple logic working on the obvious. Of course, he did not just have to make some short deductive moves from a few very wide-ranging empirical premises already provided as such. He had first to recognize that these propositions did constitute essential premises; and then, after making the deductions from them, to appreciate that these premises and these conclusions contained and linked together concepts crucial for understanding the problem of the origin of species. The premises, the concepts, the deductions, the conclusions, all are simple. To bring them together and to see the importance of the theoretical scheme so constructed was a simple matter too. But this simplicity is the simplicity of genius.

(iii) The conclusions of the deductive argument are proved beyond dispute: for though the premises are as empirical generalizations in principle open to revision, in fact, as Darwin urged in a passage quoted already, they cannot reasonably be questioned. It is therefore all the more important to appreciate what it does not prove; and hence what, at least as far as this argument is concerned, is left open to be settled by further inquiry.

It certainly does not prove that all 'the various degrees of biological improvement that we find in nature'[8] can be accounted for in these terms. It proves at most only that some 'biological improvement' must occur. Darwin needed, and provided, other facts and considerations to support his far wider and more revolutionary conclusion: 'that species are not immutable; but that those belonging to what are called the same genera are lineal descendants of some other and generally extinct species, in the same manner as the acknowledged varieties of any one species are the descendants of that species ... I am convinced that Natural Selection has been the main but no exclusive means of modification' (pp. 5–6). Though he built up a mighty case for this sweeping conclusion the case is one which could not in principle be complete unless the whole science of evolutionary biology were complete. Here the field for inquiry is open and without limit.

Again, this deductive argument has nothing to say about the causes and mechanisms of variation. Indeed the *Origin of Species* as a whole has on these little to say. Darwin begins his summary of the chapter 'Laws of Variation': 'Our ignorance of the laws of variation is profound' (p. 151). While in 'Recapitulation and Conclusion' one of the advantages of accepting his theory urged is: 'A grand and almost untrodden field of inquiry will be opened, on the causes and laws of variation, on correlation of growth, on the effects of use and disuse, on the direct action of external conditions, and so forth' (p. 437). Thus Lamarckism is quite compatible with Darwin's theory; and Darwin indeed does himself accept in the chapter on variation the inheritance of acquired characters. There would not, of course, be this elasticity had Darwin, like Julian Huxley, held a theory in which V (variation) would be replaced in the equations by M (mutation); and 'mutation' would be so defined as to exclude Lamarckism – the infamous thing! Thus, again, it would be strictly compatible with this deductive core of Darwinism to maintain that some or all favourable variations were the results of special interventions by the Management. Though any such arbitrary and anti-scientific postulations would be entirely out of harmony with Darwin's own thoroughly naturalistic spirit, and his Lyellian insistence on continuity of development: '... species are produced and exterminated by slowly acting and still existing causes, and not by miraculous acts of creation and by catastrophes ...' (p. 439). Notwithstanding the fact that in the *Origin of Species* he always concedes a special creation for the first life: '... life, with its several powers, having been breathed by the Creator into a few forms or into one ...' (p. 441); yet 'I should infer from analogy that probably all the organic beings which have ever lived on this earth have descended from some one primordial form, into which life was first breathed by the Creator' (p. 436).

(iv) Darwinism provides an outstanding example to show how a good theory guides and stimulates inquiry, setting whole new ranges of fruitful questions. This Darwin sees clearly. He rightly claims as a great advantage attending the acceptance of his theory, that: 'A grand and almost untrodden field of inquiry will be opened, on the causes and laws of variation.... A new variety raised by man will be a more important and interesting subject of study than one more species added to the infinitude of already recorded species. Our classifications will come to be, as far as they can be so made, genealogies ... we have to discover and trace the many diverging lines of descent in our natural genealogies.... Rudimentary organs will speak infallibly with respect to the nature of long lost structures.... Embryology will reveal to us the structure, in some degree obscured, of the prototypes of each great class' (pp. 437–8). Ranging further: 'In the distant future I see open fields for far more important researches. Psychology will be based on a new foundation, that of the necessary acquirement of each mental power and capacity by gradation' (p. 439).[9]

(v) Again, Darwinism makes an excellent text-book example to show how a theory explains: by showing that the elements to be explained are not after all just a lot of separate brute facts –

just one damn thing after or along with another – but rather what, granted the assumptions of the theory, is to be expected.[10]

Whereas before Darwin the general opinion even among biologists was that species constituted natural kinds, created separately:[11] he tried to show that 'Although much remains obscure, and will long remain obscure . . . the view which most naturalists entertain, and which formerly I entertained – namely, that each species has been independently created – is erroneous' (p. 5); and that, on the contrary, all species have their places on one single family tree – or at most on four or five – and are thus in the most strict and literal sense related. In what we have called the deductive core of his theory he shows how, on certain assumptions, a struggle for existence, natural selection, and some biological improvement must be expected. In applying this conceptual framework in detail in the attempt to account for the origin of species he shows how not only the existence of an enormous number of species but also many other very general biological facts previously isolated and brute are just what, granted its premises and some other equally plausible assumptions, is to be expected.

In his 'Recapitulation' (pp. 422–32) Darwin reviews some of these very general facts which he has considered earlier in more detail. For instance: 'As natural selection acts solely by accumulating slight, successive, favourable variations, it can produce no great or sudden modification. . . . Hence the canon of "*Natura non facit saltum*" [Literally: Nature does not take a jump—A. F.], whcih every fresh addition to our knowledge tends to make truer, is on this theory simply intelligible. We can see why nature is prodigal in variety, though niggard in innovation. But why this should be a law of nature if each species has been independently created, no man can explain' (p. 424: italics mine). Then: 'Looking to geographical distribution, if we admit that there has been during the long course of ages much migration . . . then we can understand, on the theory of descent with modification, most of the great leading facts in Distribution . . . we can understand, by the aid of the Glacial period, the identity of some few plants, and the close alliance of many others, on the most distant mountains, and likewise the close alliance of some of the inhabitants of the sea in the northern and southern temperate zones, though separated by the whole intertropical ocean' (pp. 428–9). And so on.

If we ask how Darwinism explains, or indeed how any other theory in the natural sciences explains, the answer seems to lie in its powers: to provide connexions between elements which without it would be unconnected–just a lot of loose and separate facts; and to show how the phenomena to be explained are, on certain assumptions, exactly what is to be expected.[12]

(vi) Darwin, always conscientious and generous in acknowledging his debts, refers several times to Malthus: '... the Struggle for Existence amongst all organic beings throughout the world, which inevitably follows from the high geometrical ratio of their increase, ... This is the doctrine of Malthus, applied to the whole animal and vegetable kingdoms' (p. 4: cf. passage on p. 9 quoted above).[13] It is therefore perhaps not surprising that the logical skeleton of theory which provided the organizing and supporting framework for all Malthus' inquiries and recommendations about population resembles in almost every respect so far considered the theoretical framework of the *Origin of Species*.

Even for those who are not antecedently inclined, either by their political and religious ideology or by their deep emotional drives, to eschew Malthusian ideas, these similarities may be obscured by the fact that Malthus' theory as he presents it himself contains several logical faults, albeit easily remediable ones. Also, unfortunately and unnecessarily, it has built into it various always controversial and now generally obnoxious value commitments. Nevertheless Malthus, like Darwin, in his theory does proceed *a priori* from very general, scarcely contestable, empirical premises. From the manifest power of the human animal to reproduce in a geometrical ratio of increase; and from an assumption, too precisely formulated as an arithmetical ratio, which expresses the fact that the possibilities of increasing the resources necessary for living are, though elastic, finite, Malthus would deduce some very important empirical conclusions (cf. (i) above). The deductive moves once the premises are assembled are not elaborate (cf. (ii) above). The limitations of the purely deductive argument are important (cf. (iii) above). For neither in Malthus' original form nor in a slightly amended and corrected form will the premises yield the conclusion that the power of increase must be checked *everywhere and always* absolutely. The same is true of the premises from which Darwin derives the conclusion that there must be a struggle for existence. These alone are not sufficient to prove that no species ever has or ever could have enjoyed *even for a short time* an environment in which its possibilities of increase were not checked by competition either from other species or from other members of the same species. They prove only that such a condition if it did ever occur must necessarily be very short lived. But whereas this qualification is on the evolutionary time scale with which Darwin was dealing insignificant: in the field of human affairs with which Malthus was concerned it may sometimes be very important indeed. For here a generation is a lifetime; and in determining practical policy some weight may properly be given to Keynes' reminder that in the long run we are all dead.

Again, the theory of Malthus, like that of Darwin, has the power to guide and stimulate inquiry, setting ranges of fruitful new questions (cf. (iv) above). Recognition of the enormous animal power of reproductive increase, and of the inescapable fact that this power must always in the fairly short run be checked at the finite though elastic limits of the possibility of increasing the resources necessary for living – if it is not checked earlier by something else: generates the master question 'How in fact is this enormous power checked?' And it was precisely this question which provoked all the empirical inquiries the results of which Malthus embodied in the second version of the *Essay on Population.*[14]

Finally, Malthus' theory too makes an excellent text-book example. It can be used to show how a theory picks out and explains by showing connexions between the vital elements in the situation. It can be used to show how granted certain conditions a theory can explain why certain other conditions also hold; by revealing that in these circumstances and on this theory these things are what is to be expected (cf. (v) above). Furthermore, it has the advantage of belonging to the field of social studies, still even more neglected by philosophers of science than biology. It can illustrate excellently the temptation confusingly and implicitly to incorporate controversial value commitments into the very structure of a theory, thereby determining the directions to be taken by any policy founded thereon. At this point the analogy between Malthus and Darwin begins to break down. It would be illuminating to develop a full Plutarchian comparison, to distinguish and catalogue the similarities and dissimilarities between the two theories. But here it is sufficient simply to mention a few of the similarities between Darwinism and a system of ideas which, partly because it is uncongenial both to the two most powerful ideological groups in the world[15] and to certain psychologically more elemental sources of prejudice,[16] is still very generally misunderstood and underestimated.[17]

The Conceptual Changes required by Darwinism

Darwinism, as again Darwin himself clearly saw, implies that we must abandon assumptions implicit in the previous use of certain categorial terms such as *genus* and *species*: 'When the views advanced by me in this volume . . . are generally admitted . . . there will be a considerable revolution in natural history. Systematists will be able to pursue their labours at at present; but they will not be incessantly haunted by the shadowy doubt whether this or that form be in essence a species' (p. 436). Which, he remarks, feelingly: 'I feel sure, and I speak after experience, will be no slight relief' (p. 436). Hence: 'I look at the term *species* as one arbitrarily given for the sake of convenience to a set of individuals closely resembling each other, and that it does not essentially differ from the term *variety*, which is given to less distinct and more fluctuating forms. The term *variety*, again, in comparison with mere individual differences, is also applied arbitrarily, and for mere convenience's sake' (p. 49: italics mine). 'Hereafter we shall be compelled to acknowledge that the only distinction between species and well-marked varieties is, that the latter are known, or believed, to be connected at the present day by intermediate gradations, whereas species were formerly thus connected' (p. 436). 'In short, we shall have to treat species in the same manner as those naturalists treat genera, who admit that genera are merely artificial combinations made for convenience' (p. 437).

The assumptions which Darwin's theory commits him to challenge are more particular cases of those very general prejudices about language and classification which Locke had begun to uncover and to question in his *Essay concerning Human Understanding* (1690). These are the assumptions: that all things belong to certain natural kinds, in virtue of their 'essential natures'; that there are no marginal cases falling outside and between these sharply delimited collections of individuals; that there must always be straight yes or no answers to the question 'Is this individual a so and so or not?'; and that men have only to uncover and, as it were, write the labels for, the classes to which nature has antecedently allocated every individual thing. To such assumptions in the biological field the pictures appropriate are: that of *Genesis,* of all creatures created after their sharply different kinds; and that of the tradition, illustrated by William Blake, of Adam naming the beasts. They would justify the approach to classification epitomized in the citation of the Swedish Academy in honouring Linnaeus: 'he discovered the essential nature of insects'. Or that of his own famous but dark saying, quoted by Darwin: '. . . the characters do not make the genus, but . . . the genus gives the characters . . .' (p. 372).

In one aspect Darwin's work can be seen as a continuation and application of that of Locke, particularly of the third book of the *Essay* 'Of Words'; though there seems to be no evidence that he had ever read the philosopher. For he is insisting on 'that old canon in natural history, "*Natura non facit saltum*"' (p. 185; cf. pp. 174–5 and p. 424); and arguing that on his theory 'we shall at least be freed from the vain search for the undiscovered and undiscoverable essence of the term *species*' (p. 437: italics mine in this and the previous quotation). Sir Arthur Keith in his Plutarchian comparison of Locke with Darwin fails surprisingly to notice this continuity.[18]

As an example of philosophy within scientific theory this analysis and reinterpretation of the concepts of *species*, *variety*, and *genus*, might be compared with Einstein's analysis of *motion* and *simultaneity* in relativity theory. In both cases the analysis is required by the theory. In both cases it had been to a greater or lesser extent anticipated by a philosopher before it was reworked and put to use by a scientist. But whereas Darwin seems never to have read Locke, Einstein certainly did read Mach; and acknowledged indebtedness to him.

The Model contained and 'deployed' in Darwinism

Recently the useful notion of the 'deployment' of a model has been introduced into the philosophy of the physical sciences. At the stage at which a new model is introduced the data that we have to go on, the phenomena which it is used to explain, do not justify us in prejudging, either way, which of the questions which normally make sense when asked of things which, say, travel will eventually be given a meaning on the new theory also. . . . One might speak of models in physics as more or less "deployed" '.[19] How far a given model is said to be deployed is a matter of how far the analogy, between that model and the phenomena to which it is applied, is believed to hold. This idea is relevant also elsewhere than in the physical sciences. The acceptance of Darwin's theory made possible a massive deployment of one model which had been curiously boxed up and impotent for an extraordinarily long time. This was the model of the family: with which was associated the method of representation employed to express both familial relationships ('the family tree') and one system of classification ('the tree of Porphyry').[20] Once again Darwin saw what he was doing: 'The terms used by naturalists of affinity, relationship, community of type, paternity . . . will cease to be metaphorical and will have a plain signification'; while 'Our classifications will come to be, as far as they can be made, genealogies . . .' (p. 437). The remarkable points about this particular model are: first, that it does not seem originally to have been introduced as any part of an attempt at scientific explanation; and, second, that its suggestive force does not seem to have had much influence towards the production of the theory which made possible its deployment. The various terms appropriate to this model were, apparently, introduced because naturalists noticed analogies which made the idea of family relationship seem apt as a metaphor. But the suggestion that the metaphor might be considerably more than a mere metaphor, that the model could be deployed, seems almost always to have been blocked by the strong resistance of the accepted doctrine of the fixity of species.

We can find in Darwin's letters and other papers indications of the strength of this resistance: though, of course, we with the advantage of hindsight see before Darwin the occasional deviations to a doctrine of descent standing out. It is a mistake to interpret this resistance simply as a matter of religion. Certainly belief in the evolution of species would be incompatible with the acceptance of the creation myths of *Genesis*, interpreted literally: (to say nothing of the incompatibility between the two myths themselves). But the evolutionary geology of Lyell is equally irreconcilable with a literal reading of the Pentateuch; and that was already becoming generally accepted among scientific men when Darwin began to work on the origin of species. Quite apart from any considerations of ideology it *is* an inescapable biological fact that living things as we now see them around us do seem, with only comparatively infrequent exceptions, to belong to various natural kinds; which mate with and reproduce, again with only comparatively minor exceptions, after their kinds. It was precisely this massive and stubborn fact which the aetiological myth makers of *Genesis* were trying to account for with their theory of the special creation of fixed species. Even after the evolutionary geologists had opened up the vast time scale needed for a smooth and uniformitarian process of biological evolution, the way of this concept was still blocked by the difficulty of suggesting any mechanisms which could possibly have brought about such an enormous development. To this problem Darwin found the clue in the concept of natural selection, suggested to him by his reading of Malthus.

Another bulwark of the doctrine of fixed species would presumably be the unevolutionary view of language referred to above. For while the general fact of the apparent stability and separateness of seeming 'natural kinds' is a main source and stay for certain false assumptions about language: those assumptions, usually hidden, would in turn support the idea of the fixity of species. For to the extent that we assume that, because a question of the 'Is this an X?' form can usually be answered by a straight 'Yes' or 'No', such a question of identification must always be susceptible of a straight yes or no answer: to this extent we are mistaking it that all the things in the world must without exception either definitely fit or definitely not fit into the classificatory pigeonholes provided by our language, labelled with the words presently available in the vocabulary of that language. This is an assumption which has only to be revealed and recognized to be challenged. Nevertheless it is one which has been, and remains, protean, powerful, and pervasive.

The 'Philosophical Implications' of Darwinism

Darwin revolutionized biological studies. But in addition, rightly or wrongly, his work has had considerable effects in shaping world outlooks and determining the general climate of opinion. This influence has been felt in two spheres. First, Darwin succeeded in indicating, at least in outline, how the appearance of design in living things might perhaps be accounted for without any appeal to actual interventions by some Supernatural Designer. Second, his ideas have been taken, or mistaken, to justify various moral and political policies.

Now it may well be that David Hume in his masterpiece, the *Dialogues concerning Natural Religion* (First edition, 1779), provided all the instruments needed to dismantle the Argument to Design. But Hume's subtle speculative arguments, presented as they are in the discreet and curiously difficult form of a philosophical dialogue, have never made much impact directly on popular thinking. Alternatively, it may well be that some version of this hardiest and most perennial of all the arguments of natural theology can be salvaged and refined for reuse, even if you have rejected absolutely the idea that supernatural interventions may be postulated to explain the particular course of nature. Nevertheless, the popular version of this argument, developed perhaps most powerfully in the *Natural Theology: or Evidences of the Existence and Attributes of the Deity collected from the Appearances of Nature* (First edition, 1802), though not of course originated by Paley, urges that just as from the observation of a watch we may infer the existence of a watchmaker, so by parity of reasoning, from the existence of mechanisms so marvellous as the human eye we must infer the existence of a Designer. Paley explicitly repudiates as an alternative any suggestion 'that the eye, the animal to which it belongs, every other animal, every plant ... are only so many out of the possible varieties and combinations of being which the lapse of infinite ages has brought into existence: that the present world is the relic of that variety; millions of other bodily forms and other species having perished, being by the defect of their constitutions incapable of preservation.... Now there is no foundation whatever for this conjecture in anything which we observe in the works of nature ...' (*Paley's Works,* 1838 edition, Vol. I, p. 32). It is this version of the Argument to Design to which the *Origin of Species* is crucially relevant. For in it Darwin offers a demonstration, backed by a mass of empirical material, of how adaptation however remarkable might be the result not of supernatural artifice but of natural selection.

Again, the doctrine of Darwinism has been taken to justify the most extraordinarily diverse, and often mutually incompatible, moral and political policies. As a purely scientific theory by itself it could not entail any normative conclusions (conclusions, that is, about what *ought* to be); because it would not, so long as it remained a purely scientific theory, contain any normative premises. Coming, however, from this important truism in the abstract to our particular case it is perhaps just worth mentioning that one or two of Darwin's scientific ideas are peculiarly open to ethical misinterpretation; though he himself is usually careful to avoid and to discourage such misconstructions.

Thus the concept of the survival of the fittest in the struggle for existence is easily mistaken to imply that Nature favours the survival of the most admirable and best. Whereas of course 'fittest' here is to be defined neutrally as 'having whatever as a matter of fact it may take to survive'. Again, because natural selection in a struggle for existence enables the fittest (in this neutral sense) to win out against their competitors, it has seemed that evolutionary biology provides a ready-made justification for unrestricted competition, and extinction take the hindmost. So it has been found necessary to compile books on mutual aid, to show that co-operation within and between species has also sometimes paid off in the biological rat race. While, on the other side, the descriptive law of the jungle has been accepted as the prescriptive law of a natural order of Nature: '. . . one general law, leading to the advancement of all organic beings, namely, multiply, vary, let the strongest live and the weakest die' (p. 219). In fact Darwinism provides no reason: either for saying that what will survive in unrestricted competition will be the most excellent and worthy; or for denying that some co-operation may pay off within the general struggle for existence. One dramatic turn of phrase does not commit Darwin to the error of regarding the laws of nature which *describe* what does go on, as laws *prescribing* what ought to go on. Again, the not particularly Darwinian notion of higher animals, combined with the Darwinian idea of their evolution by natural selection, may raise a hope that Nature is somehow in favour of progress. Of this Darwin himself was not altogether innocent. While in considering 'Geological Succession' he remarks noncommittally: 'The inhabitants of each successive period in the world's history have beaten their predecessors in the race for life, and are, insofar, higher in the scale of nature; and this may account for that vague yet ill-defined sentiment, felt by many palaeontologists, that organization on the whole has progressed' (p. 309). In his final peroratory paragraph he goes further into the world of evaluation, claiming: '. . . from the war of nature, from famine and death, the most exalted object we are capable of conceiving, the higher animal, directly follows. There is grandeur in this view of life . . .' (p. 441). Yet in pure evolutionary theory nothing is valuable and nothing is without value. By it nothing is justified, and no values are guaranteed.[21] Things just happen.

ACKNOWLEDGEMENT

I should like to express here my thanks to my colleague at Keele, Dr R. G. Evans for his helpful criticism of an earlier draft of this paper. He is in no way responsible for the biological and other errors which no doubt it still contains.

NOTES

1 See for example Stephen Toulmin's *The Philosophy of Science* (Hutchinson, 1953) .

2 All references are given to the World's Classics edition first published in 1902 by the Oxford University Press.

3 Contrast Wittgenstein in the *Tractatus Logico-Philosophicus* (Kegan Paul, 1922): 'The Darwinian theory has no more to do with philosophy than has any other hypothesis of natural science' (4.1122).

4 I particularly do *not* want to suggest that all these, and all the others classed sometimes as 'scientific' or 'theoretical' entities, enjoy exactly the same ontological status.

5 *Autobiography of Charles Darwin* (Watts, 1929), p. 75.

6 C. F. A. Pantin in *The History of Science* (Cohen and West, 1953), p. 137: italics in original.

7 Julian Huxley *The Process of Evolution* (Chatto and Windus, 1953), p. 38.

8 *Ibid.*

9 'About thirty years ago there was much talk that geologists ought only to observe and not to theorize; and I well remember someone saying that at this rate a man might as well go into a gravel pit and count the pebbles and describe the colours. How odd it is that anyone should not see that all observation must be for or against some view if it is to be of any service.' (*More Letters of Charles Darwin*, ed. Francis Darwin and A. Seward, Vol. I, p. 195.)

10 The best short study of explanation which I know is by John Hospers in *Essays in Conceptual Analysis* (Ed. Flew, Macmillan, 1956). With this may be compared Norman Campbell *What is Science?* Ch. v. (Dover Publications, New York, 1952:

the original 1921 U.K. edition has been out of print for years). Campbell's thinking is oriented towards physics and chemistry: so it may not be obvious immediately how or how far his emphatic distinction between laws (which do not explain) and theories (which do) can be applied to evolutionary biology. It is also unfortunate that he fails to make any distinction between: explaining *why* something occurs; and explaining *to* some particular person the meaning of some notion. He thus commits the howler: 'Explanation in general is the expression of an assertion in a more acceptable and satisfactory form' (p. 77). If this were so, no explanation could ever give us any new information.

11 I do not want here or elsewhere in this paper to enter into the difficult question of where exactly Darwin's originality lay. See on this J. Arthur Thomson 'Darwin's Predecessors' in *Darwin and Modern Science* (ed. A. C. Seward. C.U.P., 1909).

12 I insert the qualification 'in the natural sciences' simply in order to bypass the recent attempts to show that the second clause does not hold good of explanations in history.

13 The well-known passage in the *Autobiography* relevant here is particularly worth quoting for its timely moral to specialists inclined to neglect their general studies: 'In October 1838, that is, fifteen months after I had begun my systematic enquiry, I happened to read for amusement Malthus on *Population*, and being well prepared to appreciate the struggle for existence which everywhere goes on from long-continued observation of the habits of animals and plants, it at once struck me that under these circumstances favourable variations would tend to be preserved, and unfavourable ones to be destroyed. The result of this would be the formation of new species. Here, then, I had at last got a theory by which to work . . .' (p. 57). Compare A. R. Wallace *My Life, A Record of Events and Opinions* (London, 1905), Vol. I, p. 232, for his account of the operation of the same stimulus in his parallel case.

14 The second and all later editions are so substantially different from the first as to constitute different books. It would be good if the practice of distinguishing them as *First Essay* and *Second Essay* became general. Since the Appendices are important, the *Second Essay* is best studied in one of the later editions in which these are included: e.g. the sixth edition of 1826.

15 At the UNO World Population Conference in Rome in 1954 it was notable how often Roman Catholic and Communist delegates were found standing side by side in rejecting Malthusian ideas. For a very sober comment on the opposition of this Holy-Unholy Alliance see *World Population and Resources* (P.E.P. Reports, 1955), pp. 307 ff.

16 See J. C. Flügel *Population, Psychology, and Peace* (Watts, Thinkers' Library).

17 For an exposition and an attempt at reconstructive criticism of Malthus' theory I may perhaps be allowed to refer to my 'The Structure of Malthus' Population Theory' in *Australasian Journal of Philosophy*, 1957.

18 'Darwin's Place among Philosophers' in *Rationalist Annual 1955.*

19 Stephen Toulmin: *loc. cit.* p. 37.

20 On the importance of 'methods of representation' we may again refer to Stephen Toulmin *loc cit., passim.* The 'tree of Porphyry' was the name given both to a certain method of classification and to a way of representing this method by a sort of family tree.

21 On the subject of this last section see: Julian Huxley's 'Progress' in *Essays of a Biologist* (Chatto and Windus, 1923) and *Evolution and Ethics* (Pilot Press, 1947). This last contains a reprint of T. H. Huxley's Romanes Lecture. For a rather unsympathetic criticism see Stephen Toulmin 'World Stuff and Nonsense' in *Cambridge Journal,* Vol. I.

THE FORMATION OF ANIMAL SPECIES

A. B. ACTON

Classification

A table-knife, a carving-knife, and a pen-knife differ quite distinctly, and yet they are all knives. They all have a blade which can be used for cutting, and a handle. A dagger may still be a knife, but a sword is not; it has a different function and consequently a different shape. Most objects of everyday experience can be classified in this way: any knife, fork, or spoon is fairly easily recognized and consigned to one of these categories. We use these general names because they are convenient. Instead of saying that a silversmith makes tea-spoons, table-spoons, and dessert-spoons, we say that he makes spoons: and we lose very little information in doing so.

The zoologist is concerned with animals. If he wishes to tell some other zoologist about the work he is doing, he must be able to refer to an animal in such a way that there will be no doubt in the other's mind about what exactly this animal is. He may say that he is studying the way Albert digests his food; this tells us next to nothing. He may say that Albert is a mammal, and this tells us a little more. However, if he says that he is studying the digestive processes of a domestic cat, then any other zoologist knows exactly what animal to use if he wishes to repeat the experiments, and, just as important, he knows that within reason the conclusions which can be drawn from these experiments apply to all domestic cats. We say that all domestic cats have retractile claws, but we do not find it necessary to examine every one before we arrive at this conclusion. Because of their obvious similarity we might guess that wild-cats have retractile claws, but it would be dangerous to go much further and extend the inference to the lion.

The taxonomic categories

Spoons are easily recognized as spoons; they are similar because they serve similar functions. But how do we know that this animal is the same as that? And what do we mean by same? All animals can be grouped into categories, some wider than others. The largest groups are the phyla. As an example, the Phylum Chordata contains all those animals, like ourselves, which have a backbone, or something akin to one, and so contains dogs, cats, whales, fish, birds, frogs, and snakes, and many others. The Phylum Arthropoda contains all the animals with a hard body surface and jointed limbs. These include the insects, the crabs, lobsters, and centipedes. The phyla are referred to as the highest categories and are divided into lower categories which contain animals that resemble each other more than they resemble animals from other such groups. The lower the category, the more characters must be used to define a member of it. Thus a mammal can be recognized by a single character, its hair, but two closely related species of mammal, such as the lion and the tiger, can only be described so as to distinguish them, both from each other and from all other mammals, by a great many characters.

The Phylum Chordata contains several Classes whose members are familiar. The fishes, the amphibians (frogs and newts), the reptiles (snakes, lizards, and tortoises), the birds, and the mammals each form a Class. The classes are divided into orders, the orders into families, the families into genera, and finally the genera into species. Though the species is not quite the lowest taxonomic category, it is the basic unit which composes the higher categories. In taxonomy an animal is referred to by a double name; the first refers to the genus and the second to the species within the genus. This is partly because it would be difficult to find enough single names to cover several million different animals, but also because the generic name gives valuable information about the relationship of that particular animal to closely related animals. The domestic cat belongs to the species *Felis domesticus*, and is much more closely related to the lion *Felis leo* than, for instance, to the dog *Canis familiaris.*

All animals with feathers are birds; they belong to the Class Aves of the Phylum Chordata. Most of the familiar birds, the sparrows, crows, starlings, robins, and thrushes, belong to the Order Passeriformes; the ducks, geese, and swans form another Order, the Anseriformes. These common names belong to groups of animals which are at the level of genera or higher categories; they do not belong to closely related species. Now within one of these groups the rooks form one species, the carrion-crows another. In another group, the blackbird and the song-thrush form two distinct species. The differences between the blackbird *Turdus merula* and the song-thrush *Turdus ericetorum* are obvious. These differences include the colour, the song, and the feeding behaviour. The song-thrush cracks the shells of snails by beating them against a hard surface; the blackbird never does this. But how many people know the difference between the song-thrush and the mistle-thrush? These again are species of a single genus. Apart from the rare piebald and white forms, all blackbirds look alike and different from other birds. It is not difficult to see that all blackbirds belong to a single group within which there appears to be no subdivision; this group is the species. The thrushes at first sight look the same, but if the song-thrush and the mistle-thrush are once seen side by side, and if the differences are pointed out, the reason for splitting an apparently homogeneous group becomes clear. The birds within each of these two groups are similar, and there is no reason to divide the groups further; these groups are species.

Natural or arbitrary?

The wild-cat *Felis catus* is obviously closely related to the leopard *F. pardus*, but what about the cheetah? It looks like a leopard, though in fact it resembles the dog in a number of ways, the most obvious being the claws which cannot be withdrawn as a cat's can. Here a judgement has to be made, and accordingly the cheetah is consigned to a separate group, a genus, of which it is the only living member, and called *Cynaelurus jubatus.* A decision of this sort is fairly easily arrived at, but is the criterion merely an arbitrary one of expediency, or are there categories to which every animal inevitably belongs, just as every soldier does? He may be a private or a sergeant or a field-marshal, but there is no soldier who does not bear some rank. Furthermore, there is no doubt about whether a soldier is one rank or another; he cannot fall somewhere in between.

At some stage in the ancestry of the mammals there would be animals without hairs. A close examination of these animals during the transition might reveal that on this character alone one generation would be judged to be reptiles and their progeny to be mammals. If the transition were more gradual, one would find reptiles and mammals, and animals of doubtful status. Even if a number of other characters, such as the presence or absence of a shelled egg or of mammary glands, or the number of bones in the lower jaw, are considered as well, there will still be animals which do not obviously belong to one group or the other. However, this difficulty will only arise if evolution at this stage is gradual: if a mammal arises in a single step from a reptile then identification will be as certain as is that of a soldier's rank.

As it happens, there is no dispute over the higher categories to which an animal belongs. A dog belongs without question to the Phylum Chordata and the Class Mammalia. There are no cold-blooded birds which suckle their young. Cold-bloodedness is a characteristic of all animals apart from the birds and mammals, and only the mammals suckle their young. The higher categories in this sense are as definite as the categories of soldiers. This is either because the transitional forms, which will be few, are never found, or because evolution at this stage is not gradual. While there are few biologists who believe that sudden gross changes have been widespread, such changes are by no means disproved, and in some instances are generally accepted. The immature forms of many animals are markedly different from the adult; the caterpillar bears little resemblance to the moth, and the young tadpole little resemblance to the frog. If some of the normally immature animals in a population were to develop no further and if they at the same time became reproductively mature, they would be so different from the old reproductively mature form that they might not be able to mate with it. They would, of course, be able to mate with each other, and a new systematic category would have been formed in a single step. The old mature form would continue to produce the old immature stage. We can perhaps see such a change, though much less revolutionary, in ourselves: man differs most obviously from the other primates in the large size of his brain, compared with the rest of his body, and his sparse hair, both of which are seen in the very young ape.

The boundaries of the lower categories, the family and genus, are not nearly so well defined, and here the charge of arbitrariness can easily be made to stick. To some extent this is true of classes and even phyla, not only for the reason already given, that there must at one time have been some animals which just as well belong to one group as another, but also because we look at transitional forms at a time when we know the subsequent history of the group. The earliest birds are separated from the reptiles on the evidence that they had feathers; whether they were warm-blooded we shall never know. At the earliest stage in their evolution there would have been little good reason to divide them from their ancestors as a separate class, just as there is no reason now to separate the bats from the other mammals. Further evidence of the arbitrary nature of some of the categories can be seen when orders of different classes are compared. The sparrow, seagull, and the swan belong to different orders, and yet so do the lion, the elephant, and the whale. There is a case, though perhaps not a very good one, for classifying the birds as an order of reptiles, and not as a class on their own.

The species

The basic unit in all these categories is the species. Though this is accepted, there is still a certain amount of disagreement about what the species itself is. This disagreement arises in part because the species may sometimes be divisible into smaller units, and in part over the purely practical matter of the number of tests which may reasonably be applied in their identification. Many of the arguments over species concern their names only, and not their extent: in general it is accepted that the species is the most permanent of the taxonomic categories. Most will go further and say that it has a reality in nature as well as in the museum. Thus many of the species which were recognized and named by Linnaeus in 1789 are still accepted, though Linnaeus based his classification, not on the theory of evolution, but on a belief in the fixity of species.

A child looks the same at the end of the day as he did at the beginning. After fifty years he may be unrecognizable, but there is no doubt that he is the same person throughout. A species changes slowly and continuously, and remains the same species. But species arise from other species, so that there must be a stage when discontinuity is introduced. A child matures, but the production of a new child is a very different process from that of straightforward growth. Are we to look for a change of this sort to explain the formation of new species, or are the slow everyday changes which a species undergoes themselves sufficient? A species, however, unlike a child, is not a single individual. It is a collection of individuals: it can be divided into halves, and we can still speak of the individuals of both halves as belonging to the same species. The halves will continue to evolve; and if they evolve differently the time may come when they can no longer be called one species.

Why do all the races of man belong to a single species? The differences between an Australian aboriginal and a European are too obvious to mention. Such differences are recognized colloquially, if not in taxonomy; does it really matter whether we call the populations species, races, or tribes? It is, however, obvious that the discontinuity which distinguishes species is not mere heterogeneity. Some of us have blue eyes, others brown. No one would seriously maintain that males and females should be different species, yet in some animals the differences between them are so striking that they have through lack of knowledge been put in different genera. The point is that all such variation is united by a single factor, heredity; any of the alternatives can be found among brothers and sisters. There is complete fertility within the species *Homo sapiens*. On the other hand there is no interbreeding between the zebra, *Equus zebra*, and the horse *E. caballus*. Though the hybrid (the mule or hinny) between *E. caballus* and *E. asinus* is as robust as either parent, it is sterile. There is some barrier to reproduction between species. Mules are not born of mules.

The newt *Triturus cristatus* of Europe and Asia meets the Spanish *T. marmoratus* in a restricted area in France. Viable hybrids are found, but they are very rare. This example differs from that of the mule because the newts are nearly always found in different geographical areas, whereas the horse and ass occur together (the effect of man on the distribution of these animals is ignored here). The latter pair of species is sympatric; the newts are allopatric except for a small sympatric zone. Is the distinction between the newts made possible because they never meet, or because they can seldom breed successfully when they do? The difference between these alternatives is fundamental: if two distinct populations of animals are able to live side by side and never interbreed, they must be species, but if two distinct populations never meet, are they species or only geographical variants of a single species, that is subspecies or races? In the example of the newts, the evidence has to be examined and a decision made. This is why Darwin made the remark about the species being what a competent taxonomist considered it to be.

The common sparrow *Passer domesticus* is found alongside the willow sparrow *P. hispaniolensis* in Spain, Greece, Asia Minor, and Palestine. They look different and they never interbreed in these areas so that they are considered to be separate species. However in northern Africa the sparrows interbreed freely and more hybrids may be found in a population than birds of the parent forms. The decision has become rather more difficult; one evolutionist considers that they clearly belong to one species, another that they are even more clearly different species. The carrion-crow *Corvus corone* and the hoodie-crow *C. cornix* again look quite different, but meet in only a small part of their range; here they interbreed freely. It is not surprising that the decision has not always been in favour of full specific rank.

Can the species be defined?

These examples range from the unequivocal to the controversial. At some stage in this series reproductive isolation breaks down, though in the example of the sparrows in a maddeningly irregular way. Individuals of undoubtedly different species never interbreed, individuals of the same species always interbreed, and somewhere between these two extremes there may be a dividing line. If we attempt to define a species on the basis of its reproductive isolation, we shall at least avoid having to make a decision about the relative importance of various external differences. The races of man appear to differ from each other much more than do the species of tit, the great-tit, the marsh-tit, and the coal-tit, and yet the tits are good species and the races of man are not.

However, the species of tit are reproductively isolated; morphological difference and reproductive isolation are often associated. This at once explains the ability of the taxonomist to name species which are acceptable by any standard, but it brings us back to the question of why the difficult species cannot be settled by just any convenient criterion, provided that the same one is used by all taxonomists. This view has its advocates; the idea of naming a species on any character apart from its appearance seems to some to be ludicrous. And yet there is still disagreement. We have reached the stage when we can go no further without some idea of how species are formed in nature.

Variation within a species

Professor Moore has made an extensive study of the leopard-frog *Rana pipiens* in the United States, and he finds that if leopard-frogs from Vermont, north of New York, are mated with similar frogs from Wisconsin, some 800 miles west, or New Jersey, some 300 miles south, their fertility is, as might be expected, quite normal. There is no difference between these crosses and one of frogs from the same pond. When the parents come from Vermont and Louisiana, 1,300 miles to the southwest, the rate of development of the embryos is slowed and there are morphological defects which, however, are not sufficient to affect their viability seriously. When frogs from Vermont and Florida, 1,200 miles apart, are used, the morphological defects are so great that many of the embryos die. When the frogs come from even farther away not one of the embryos may develop to maturity. If crosses are made between frogs from within any of these areas, as for example frogs from central and southern Florida, the embryos develop quite normally. Lastly, when a male from Vermont is crossed with a female from Mexico, nearly all the embryos die in the earliest stages of development. These frogs are undoubtedly of the same species. They look the same and individuals from any adjacent regions are able to interbreed normally.

The herring-gull *Larus argentatus* of western Europe interbreeds with a slightly different gull in North America. The difference between them is sufficient to deserve recognition and the two are separated as subspecies. There is a further subspecies in eastern Russia which interbreeds with the American to the east and with another in Scandinavia. The subspecies in Scandinavia interbreeds, not with *L. argentatus*, but with the lesser black-backed gull *L. fuscus*. *L. fuscus* itself occurs alongside *L. argentatus* in Europe and seldom interbreeds. Thus two quite distinct gulls are nevertheless connected by a long chain of intermediate forms between none of which is it easily possible to draw a line that would divide the whole series into two clear species: and because of this some people will prefer to call them all by the same name.

The similarity between the widely separated populations of frog and those of the gulls is obvious. Biological similarity implies a sharing of a large part of the complex of hereditary determinants which is potentially available. Identical twins have identical gene complexes; brothers and sisters have only a large part in common; distant populations of leopard-frogs have less in common than nearby populations. If for some reason the intermediate populations of frog were to disappear, leaving only two isolated groups, would the conditions then be favourable for the eventual formation of two species?

Species formation?

Many biologists would say yes, and they would imagine the following course of events. Already, the southern populations differ from the northern in having a greater resistance to the effects of high temperatures, and in having a slower rate of development at low temperatures. In other words they show signs of being adapted to their environment; the north is colder than the south. Because of these differences, or other physiological differences like them, a hybrid embryo will inherit a complement of genes, half of which are adjusted to function in an animal from the north, and half in an animal from the south. These two sets of genes never come together under normal conditions and their actions may quite likely be discordant. The result is that the hybrid is at a disadvantage; as we have seen it may die young.

Once the species has become separated into two groups, each individual can only contribute genetic material to half of the species. This not only halves the store of variability which is available, but it also consolidates the variability which remains. Where once complexes of genes were able to leak from the central area of the range in all directions, they can now leak only to the border of one population, and never across to the other group. Where previously individuals were liable to find themselves anywhere in the central part of the overall range, they now can be only north or south of the barrier which we have supposed to have arisen. To be sufficiently adapted to the climate which they would normally experience before the barrier arose, the frogs would have to be able to tolerate conditions on both sides of the line. Once the barrier is up, conditions south of the line become irrelevant to the frogs living in the north, and they can become more closely adapted to the now more restricted range of conditions. The same will be happening to the south, and gradually the two groups will diverge.

Suppose now that the barrier breaks down. Frogs from north and south will meet and there will be interbreeding. If the result is the same as that which is even now found between frogs from

Mexico and Vermont, there will be no hybrid offspring. Like will continue to beget like. The fact that one set of frogs is adapted to one climate, and the other set to another, will serve to keep them in different territories. The frogs can now meet and yet remain genetically independent. From now on there is no reason why the two groups of frogs should not continue this process, together with one of steady slow adaptation to their environment (which may change!) in complete reproductive isolation. They will never again make a mutual contribution to evolution; like the newts *Triturus cristatus* and *T. marmoratus* they are now allopatric species.

If the result of interbreeding is less drastic, perhaps like that when frogs from Vermont and Louisiana are crossed, hybrids with very slight defects will be produced, though otherwise quite viable. But what sort of environmental conditions will be the most suitable for these hybrids, according to their hereditary endowment; the one in which they find themselves, or some other? One parent will be adapted to conditions in the north and one to conditions in the south. When both parents come from the same region their offspring will, like them, be adapted to conditions in that region. However, when the parents come from different regions the efficiency of their offspring under conditions to which neither parent is fully adapted is unpredictable. If the hybrid's inheritance is such that it enables it to live under any of the conditions which it is likely to experience, the reproductive isolation will break down and a single interbreeding group, a single species, will be re-established, though with slight changes. While the groups were apart, different combinations of genes will have been formed and these can now come together. Possibly these new combinations will be better than any which could have been formed in the earlier breeding system; they may spread, and the species will settle just a little more firmly into its niche. For this, and other reasons, it has been considered that the most favourable breeding system for evolutionary advance is that of a species divided into small, partially isolated, populations. The isolation must be sufficient to enable the populations to develop different gene combinations without interference, and yet it must not be so complete that the combinations once produced cannot be handed round. A species which is in effect a single breeding group can only become adapted to the average of the range of conditions which it is likely to meet; a species subdivided into smaller units may become adapted to almost any of the habitats in its range.

If the hybrids which are formed after the barrier breaks down are less well adapted than their parents, they will on the whole leave fewer offspring. Parents who might have left offspring which were as adapted as themselves will have wasted part of their reproductive potential in miscegenation. Any inherited characteristic which prevents this wastage will be maintained at the expense of one which allows hybrids to be formed. At first the hybrids may be less fertile so that they leave fewer offspring to compete with their cousins. Later, fewer hybrids will be formed, and eventually perhaps there will be no mating at all between northern and southern frogs, so that not even the eggs and sperms are wasted. *Drosophila pseudoobscura* and *D. persimilis* seem never to interbreed in the wild, but at low temperatures fairly large numbers of hybrids are produced under laboratory conditions. These hybrids are sterile. Dr Koopman has shown that if equal numbers of the two species are put in the same cage, in the first generation roughly a third of the flies are hybrids. If a second generation is produced, this will arise only from flies which mate with their own species; those that do not, produce sterile offspring. In the second generation only about a fifth of the flies are hybrid, and after the sixth generation or so less than a twentieth. This experiment shows that it is possible to intensify reproductive isolation, though this is not the same thing as bringing it into existence. It is significant that the isolating mechanisms between some allopatric species are most effective just where the species actually meet.

What keeps species apart?

Some of the factors which keep species apart are less obvious than the one we have examined. *Drosophila pseudoobscura* lives in the lowlands and on the lower mountain slopes, and is usually found in warm sunny places. *D. persimilis* lives higher up the mountains and in contrast with *D. pseudoobscura* is usually found in the cooler shadier spots. Though their geographical ranges overlap, because of these differences in habitat individuals of the two species are unlikely to meet each other, and if they do not meet they cannot mate. Male fiddler-crabs have an enormously enlarged 'pincer'; when this claw is waved in the air the females of the same species, and that species only, are attracted. The males of different species wave their claws differently and a trained observer can recognize over a score of species from this difference in behaviour. The members of one species may be quite indifferent to the antics or markings of another.

The finches of the Galápagos Islands, sometimes called Darwin's finches, are a fairly convincing testimony to the power of slight geographical barriers to keep populations apart (see Lack 1947). There are over twelve of these islands in a group lying 600 miles west of the coast of South America. The islands are inhabited by various species of finch which, though obviously closely related, are each adapted to a quite distinct way of living. Some feed on large seeds, others on small seeds, some eat fruit, some catch insects, and some pick them from the bark of trees. With practice it is possible to tell the type of food one of these birds eats from its beak. Those that eat seeds have stout bills and those, for instance, which eat fruit have a bill something like a parrot's. None of these birds is found on the mainland and so, it is thought, they must have evolved from a small number of migrants which happened at some time to reach the islands. If the type of habitat to which the migrants were accustomed did not occur on any of the islands, the birds which arrived at one would perhaps take to eating seeds and those which arrived at another to eating fruit. If the birds from the two islands did not fly from one to the other, the two populations might quite rapidly become adapted to their new surroundings. With time their hereditary mechanisms might become so different that when, for some reason, such as shortage of food, they invaded each other's territory, they might not be able to interbreed. Even if the reproductive isolation were not, so to speak, ready-made, it might develop subsequently. There are now two species. One of these might invade a third island and take to another food. With at least twelve islands it is not hard to imagine the evolution of the fourteen species which are now found among them.

Cocos Island lies about as far from the mainland as the Galápagos archipelago. This is a single island, but it offers as much variety of habitat as all the Galápagos islands put together. Again there is a species of finch which is not found on the mainland, but it occurs alone: a single small island has few physical barriers. Furthermore, the central, closely spaced, islands of the Galápagos group share most of the species; the outermost, and more scattered, islands have species on them which are found nowhere else. This is just as would be expected if physical barriers are a vital factor in the formation of species.

Are gradual changes sufficient?

The sicklebills of Hawaii are even more striking. Among them is a bird which has a short finch-like beak and another with a curved beak almost a third as long as the bird's overall length. The first bird feeds on seeds and the second on nectar. No matter what the feeding habits of the common ancestor of these birds is thought to be, whether it fed on seeds or nectar or neither, or whatever shape of beak it had, it is not easy to imagine how a bird with a short bill, which feeds on hard nuts, and also a bird with a sickle-shaped bill, which feeds on nectar, come to evolve by small gradual changes from a common ancestor.

Let us suppose that the common ancestor had a beak like a sparrow's. This bird would presumably take to food for which its beak were unsuitable only if the usual food were no longer available. If the usual food were available there would be no reason why the beak should change. The bird is now forced to eat something else; its beak is unsuitable and so would be improved by a change. Unless this change is rapid the bird and its progeny may soon die out. If the change is by large steps there is no difficulty in understanding how the shape of the beak will evolve rapidly enough to be of benefit to its owner. But large rapid changes are almost unknown.

The differences between the leopard-frogs from different parts of the United States are fairly simple ones, which need involve nothing more than a change in the rate of some internal process. Most of the differences which we can observe between animals of the same species are simple; simple differences may accumulate to form more complex ones, but take place so slowly that we cannot hope to watch them. Indeed the changes must necessarily be slight. An animal is a perfectly co-ordinated system of structures and processes; if it were not it would die. A television set is far less complicated and yet a slight haphazard change will return it to the shop. Some large changes have been seen under experimental conditions, but they would not be tolerated in nature. Small gradual changes are well known, but can they accumulate with sufficient rapidity to be effective?

In a changing environment a species must also change if it is to remain adapted. The spread of a black form of the peppered-moth *Biston betularia* from extreme rarity to the complete exclusion of the normal form in just over a hundred years has closely followed the increasing blackness of the countryside in industrial areas and is possibly the best known example of such a change (see Kettlewell 1955). Given time, and there seems to have been no lack of it, surely even the most intellectually outrageous characters could be produced by the same process? A sicklebill feeding on nectar may be forced by a shortage of flowers to turn to something else. Its beak is quite clearly useless for cracking nuts, but the fact that we can think of no suitable alternative food does not mean that there is none, or more important, that there *was* none. There are fish which are able to stun their prey by a sudden electrical discharge from certain organs. Here is a parallel with the birds' beaks; of what use was an electric organ when it could produce a barely perceptible amount of energy? Recently it was discovered by Dr Lissmann that some fish which live in muddy water, where their eyes are of little use, are able to orient themselves by means of a 'radar' system. The basis of this 'radar' is an electric organ of very low power. The gap in our knowledge has been made good; is there any reason why all the other gaps should not, in the same way, be in our knowledge of circumstances rather than in our understanding of heredity?

Are all species comparable?

But still there is dissent. No one has yet made a species in the laboratory, but using the experiments of nature the biologist has made one in his mind's eye. The circumpolar ring of subspecies of gull which connects the full species at each end is one of these experiments. Always they concern situations which can be interpreted in more than one way; they concern the doubtful species and the unusual circumstances; they concern the experiments which seem not to have quite succeeded. The successful experiments can tell us nothing. The apparatus has been packed away and the raw materials have combined to give something new. But what if the 'unsuccessful' experiments are not unsuccessful after all; they may be of a completely different type from the others? The northern and southern populations of leopard-frog are fitted to survive under the conditions in which they live, though these are not the same throughout the range of the species. The partial reproductive isolation between distant populations of them differs only in degree from that between many so-called species in nature. If we unite all the doubtful species into more comprehensive groups (the two species of gull and their subspecies would form one) the gaps between the species that remain seem to some to be of an entirely different nature from the ones we have discussed at such length. The differences between the blackbird and the song-thrush concern their colour, their song, the way they move, the colour of their eggs and their ability to break snail-shells. The two birds are not known to interbreed in the wild. However, any species which interbreed where they meet, the doubtful species, are bound to have some characters which grade into each other, if only for the obvious reason that hybrids are formed. The gaps between 'good' species, sometimes called 'bridgeless gaps', can be bridged by assuming that they differ only in degree from those between 'doubtful' species, but we can also with some reason start looking for an entirely different evolutionary process.

Sudden large changes

Most of the inherited changes which are seen in animals are small, but it has been estimated that the number of large successful changes which would be necessary to account for all the species that have ever existed is only of the order of one every fifty years or so. The number of such changes which might arise but which would fail to form new species would be greater than this, perhaps much greater than this, but the unsuccessful changes, particularly as they are large, would probably last no longer than a part of the normal life cycle of an individual, or possibly also of some of its brothers and sisters. The fact that this individual would be confined to a tiny part of the earth's surface, perhaps under a stone at the foot of your garden, easily explains why such changes have never been seen. And if large changes in fact occur, there is no reason why they should give rise exclusively to species. In fact there is no reason apart from its much greater improbability why even phyla should not be formed in a single step. However, the objections come mainly from geneticists, firstly because there is no clearly understood genetic basis for the changes, and secondly because it is difficult to see how the animal could survive a drastic upset in its normal functioning.

Every animal starts life as a single cell containing a double set of genes. This cell divides to form two, these in turn divide to form four, and eventually an adult animal of several million such cells is formed. Within the animal are organs with very different functions; the liver, the heart, and the brain resemble each other only in that they are composed of cells. And yet these cells have identical sets of genes: when the cell divides, the genes divide in such a way that (with a few exceptions) an identical set is produced. Identical twins start life as the same cell which later divides to form two embryos. We can no longer think of the gene as a factor which controls this or that character inevitably. The effect which a gene has during growth may be predictable so long as nothing else in the animal changes. If, for instance, some part of the animal's food which is essential to the normal functioning of this gene is withheld, the gene may not exert any influence at all.

A gene's most intimate surroundings include its fellow genes. A change in one may alter the effect of another; the two together may change the nature of the cell in which they occur; the change in the cell may alter the effect of further genes, which in their turn change the nature of the organ they compose. During growth a cell's surroundings alter continually as other cells are added. Because of these interactions a simple change may have profound effects on the development of the organism. Some of these effects may be adaptive and some may even produce a new species. This does not ask too much of the mechanisms of heredity, but we must believe that these gross changes are so rare as to be not often encountered.

The environment in evolution

The blacksmith has muscular arms, but unless the blacksmith's son is himself a blacksmith his arms will be like anyone else's. The adaptation is acquired, but not transmitted. Nevertheless, if the ability to acquire an adaptation is inherited, the evolutionary effect is the same. In fact under some conditions it may be more efficient to be plastic: many characters are acquired very rapidly and can be lost just as rapidly, like the blacksmith's muscles, when they are no longer of value. However, many of an animal's adaptations are inherited; the giraffe's long neck is the most famous example. If such adaptations could be acquired as the blacksmith's muscles are, and at the same time become heritable, the speed of evolution would be very much increased. It would no longer be necessary to wait until a suitable genetic change arose, nor then to wait for other changes to perfect the first: the chance that a whole, perfectly adapted, organ will arise by known genetic processes in one stroke is negligible. Though such ideas are older than Darwinism itself, there is very little evidence to support them. Evolution it seems must wait for its raw material. But a character which arises as a direct adaptation is obviously of value. If it arises generation after generation the way is then open for a genetic basis for this adaptation to evolve by the perfectly orthodox process of natural selection. A character which does not exist cannot be selected for. It might of course be asked why, if the adaptation already turns up in every generation, there would then be any value in its inheritance.

Lack of evidence need be no deterrent to the acceptance of a hypothesis, provided the process contained within the hypothesis seems to offer something which no other process can. This something is the increase in the speed of evolution brought about by the direct action of the environment on the evolving animal, but also, it is claimed, the removal of the difficulty in understanding how an organ, if it arises gradually, can be of any use in the early stages. What would be the function of a bird's feather when the first unrecognizable rudiment appeared? And if it had no function why was it maintained? We have already seen the other answer to the problem. The known hereditary mechanisms are sufficient in appropriate circumstances: we must assume that we know too little of very early history.

In conclusion

The species we have considered are living species. They may be groups of animals which look so different from other groups that for convenience in referring to them we give them names. Because they are so different from other groups there is never any difficulty in recognizing them. If the characteristics of one group change, they never change to those of a contemporary group. Or we can regard the species as being a group of organisms which is reproductively isolated from other such groups. Often a species can be recognized by either criterion, since one property in part determines the other. Species which live side by side are much more easily defined than those whose territories lie apart. Among the allopatric species are the doubtful species, and from them we get most of our information about how species are formed. But what about the animals which reproduce without a sexual process, and what about the species which the palaeontologist recognizes? Are these the same as the ones we have considered? And is the process of geographical isolation the only one which produces species?

All these questions have some sort of an answer. You have only to read on to find them.

FOR FURTHER READING

Cain, A. J. 1954. *Animal species and their evolution.* London, Hutchinson's University Library.

Dowdeswell, W. H. 1955. *The mechanism of evolution.* London, Heinemann.

Kettlewell, H. B. D. 1955. 'How industrialization can alter species.' *Discovery,* December 1955; or 1956, 'Evolution in action.' *Times Science Review*, Spring 1956.

Lack, D. 1947. *Darwin's finches.* Cambridge University Press.

Sheppard, P. M. 1958. *Natural selection and heredity*. London, Hutchinson.

ADVANCED TEXTS

Dobzhansky, T. 1951. *Genetics and the origin of species,* 3rd Edn. Columbia University Press.

Goldschmidt, D. 1940. *The material basis of evolution.* Yale University Press.

Mayr, E. 1942. *Systematics and the origin of species.* Columbia University Press.

THE ORIGIN OF ISOLATION

J. HESLOP HARRISON

AMONG the misapprehensions most common with those whose acquaintance with Darwin's work is mostly at second-hand is the belief that he assumed a general principle of blending inheritance, according to which, in any cross between unlike individuals, the characters of the parents blended with each other like ink and water, never again to separate. The fact is that Darwin was quite well aware of what we would now call mendelian segregation. He knew that parental characteristics could appear again in the progeny of a hybrid; in fact he encountered segregation of this kind in his own experiments with plants, certainly in clear enough form to disabuse him of any idea that characters invariably become blended in hybrids never again to appear in 'pure' state in their descendants. What he did conclude was that the character differences which did not 'fuse' in inheritance – that is, those which showed clear-cut segregaton in hybrid progeny – were of the nature of spontaneously arising aberrations, not of the same order as the differences which exist between species, or between races 'which have been slowly formed by man's selection, and therefore resemble to a certain extent natural species'. The distinction is a critical one, and it is clearly made in a passage in *Variation of Animals and Plants under Domestication*. In modern genetical terms, it is a distinction between the type of inheritance found when major differences in parental character are determined by differences in one or a few genes, and that which results when the dissimilarity of the parents depends upon large numbers of co-ordinated gene differences. As Darwin recognized, differences of the former character may indeed arise suddenly, as the result of mutation; those of the latter type – characteristic of species and well-established races – are the product of generations of selection working over mutations which individually have relatively minor effects.

Blending, then, to Darwin, was what happened when two inter-fertile races were allowed to cross. The ultimate product he supposed would be a population of uniform character, more or less intermediate between the parents. Races which were separated from each other geographically would be unable to blend in this manner, and so would retain their individuality. Should they be brought together, free intercrossing would ensue, with a resultant destruction of racial character. But this did not happen in most of the cases known to Darwin of closely allied species inhabiting the same area, and he was led accordingly to realize that such species must be restrained from intercrossing by some other factor than spatial separation, and, indeed, that the establishment of such a restraint was a pre-requisite for the co-existence of different species as distinct entities in the same locality.

To the extent, then, that biological species constitute populations of potentially interbreeding organisms which do not breed with other populations, their independent existence depends upon factors which preserve their breeding integrity; and these factors may be extrinsic or intrinsic. This distinction into what is externally and what internally determined is an important one. In the Darwinian sense, 'isolation' meant spatial separation; something imposed upon different populations merely because of their occupancy of different parts of the earth's surface. Today, because we have come to use the term isolation in a wider sense to cover all forms of separation of organisms into independent mating groups, this is referred to as *geographical* or *spatial* isolation. Evidently as a factor checking interbreeding it can be of any degree of efficiency according to the distance apart of the populations and the mobility of their members. But the essential feature is that geographical isolation does not depend upon *inherent* differences between the populations. All other forms of segregation of breeding groups do depend upon the existence of inherent differences – bars to free intercrossing operating, as Darwin said, through sexual aversion, mutual sterility or other such factor. Isolation of this type is commonly termed *reproductive* or *physiological.*

Because of the evolutionary importance of isolation, the methods by which reproductive isolation is achieved have been studied intensively in recent decades in a range of organisms, plant and animal. Several classifications of these 'isolating mechanisms', as they have been called by Dobzhansky, have been proposed, and for full accounts the reader should consult the works of Huxley (1942), Mayr (1942), Stebbins (1950), Dobzhansky (1956) and the various essays touching on the topic in *The New Systematics* (1940). Here we will briefly review some of the principal features of reproductive isolation, as a prelude to discussing some current problems concerning its origin and evolutionary significance.

Broadly, amongst cross-fertilized sexual organisms the interbreeding of different populations may be inhibited for any of five reasons other than simple spatial separation:

(*a*) Crossing is prevented because the two forms, whilst occurring in the same geographical region, occupy different habitats, and so do not come into contact. This may be termed ecological isolation.

(*b*) Crossing is prevented because the two forms do not reach sexual maturity at the same time: seasonal or temporal isolation.

(*c*) Crossing is prevented because, in animals, of behavioural or structural incompatibility which inhibits copulation, or, in plants, of floral differences which prevent pollination.

(*d*) Copulation or pollen transfer takes place, but fertilization fails.

(*e*) Fertilization occurs, but the egg fails to develop normally, or the hybrid does not survive, or is wholly or partly sterile.

(*a*) *Ecological isolation*

Two populations are ecologically isolated when genetically determined differences in habitat preference establish that the members of one shall not normally be present within the territory of the other. Ecological isolation thus involves spatial segregation, although the populations may be sympatric* in the sense that their habitats interdigitate very closely, forming a mosaic within a common area. The essential difference from geographical isolation lies in the fact that geographical isolation may arise initially without any differentiation of the populations; ecological isolation pre-supposes that genetical differences determining habitat preferences do exist, and thus that some evolutionary divergence has already taken place.

Evidently the closer the ecological specialization and the more sharply distinguished the habitats, the less will be the cross-breeding and the more perfect the isolation. Restriction to a special habitat is perhaps most complete among parasites with very narrow host preferences; and indeed the particular case of food-plant preference in insects has been the subject of much discussion and some experiment as a test-case of ecological isolation. But it is not enough that there should be segregation of the different populations during some periods of the life-cycle if this does not effectively check cross-breeding; thus in Lepidoptera strong food-plant preferences in larval stages would not provide reproductive isolation should the mobile adults be promiscuous. Indeed, it is doubtful whether larval food preference could ever act as an isolating mechanism, without reinforcement by some other factor, in any instance where the areas occupied by individual colonies in their specialized habitats are substantially less than the effective cruising range of adults. Correspondingly, among plants, differences in ecological tolerance would by themselves form no effective bar to crossing if the spatial segregation they imposed in any particular area were to be substantially less than the average dispersal range of pollen. For this reason, ecological specialization forms a less effective barrier in wind pollinated plants with high pollen outputs and dispersal ranges, like grasses and trees, than in insect pollinated species, in which pollen output is usually lower and dis-

* *Sympatric:* a term introduced by Poulton, meaning occupying the same country or geographical region. *Allopatric:* occupying different countries or regions.

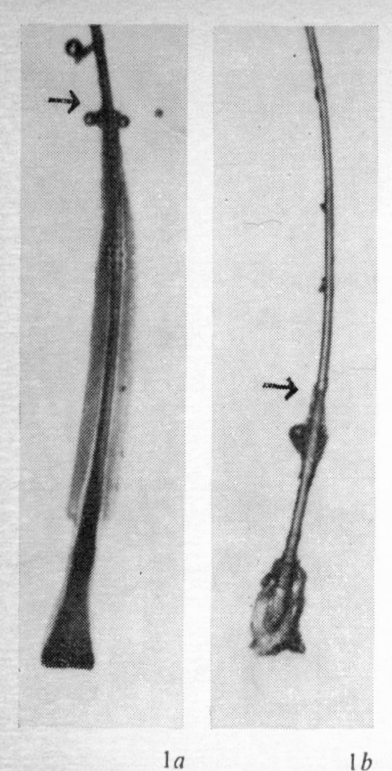

1 *a* and *b*. Hair follicles plucked from the human scalp. *a*. An actively growing follicle. The arrow marks the approximate level of the skin surface. Note the sheaths surrounding the hair shaft and the well-developed bulb at the lower end. *b*. A resting follicle. The arrow again marks the skin surface level and shows that the resting follicle is less deeply embedded in the skin than the growing phase. The entire shaft is keratinized and ends in a swelling surrounded by epithelial tissue. 1 *c*. Melanin granules isolated from dark human hair. Photographed under the electron microscope. The granules are shadowed by low-angle spattering with metal. Note variation in size and shape of granules, the longest of which are rather less than 1/1000th mm. long.

1*a* 1*b* 1*c*

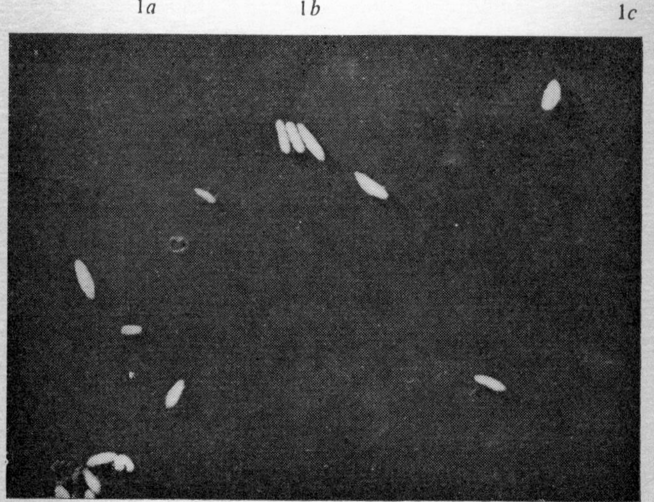

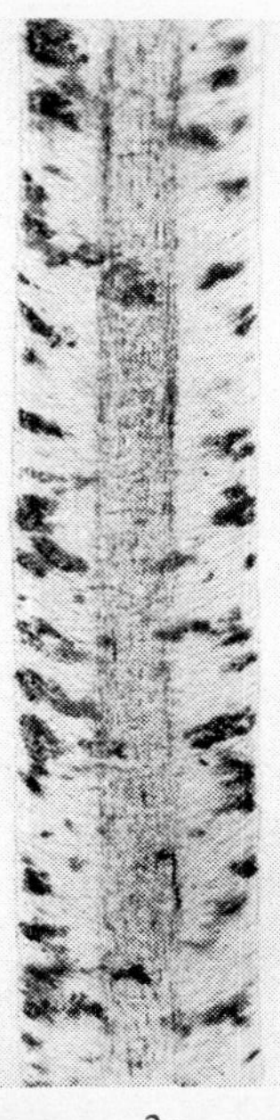

2a

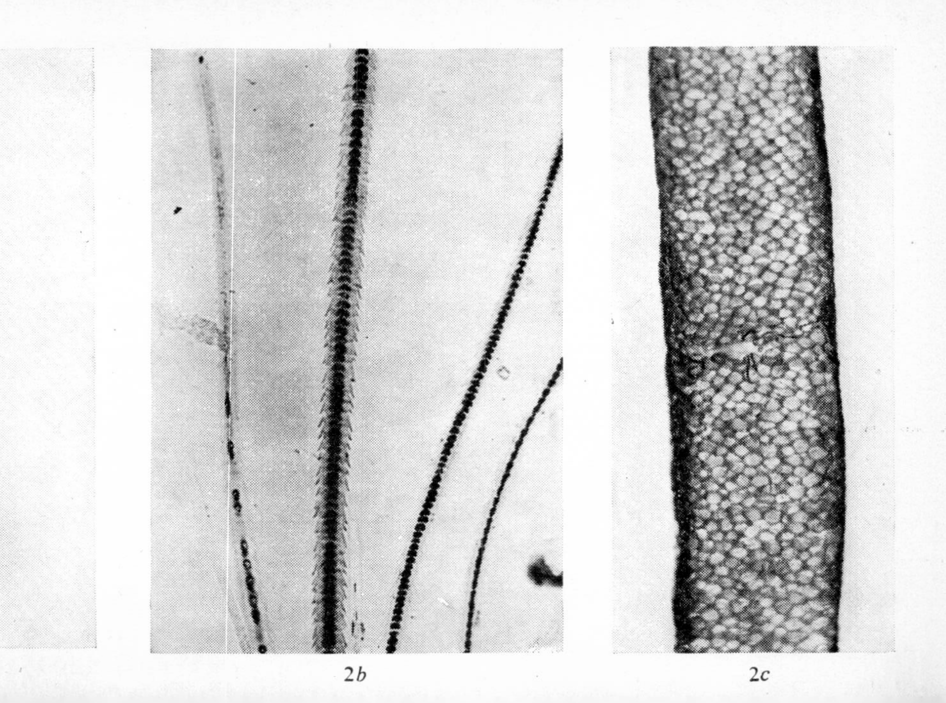

2b

2c

Photomicrographs of animal hairs. The specimens were kindly provided by the Zoological Society, London, and photographed by Mr J. Armstrong.

2*a*. Portion of a single hair shaft of a sloth (*Bradypus tridactylus*). Note the green algae embedded in the thick superficial layer of the hair.

2*b*. Hairs from a bat (*Cynopterus brevicaudatus*). Note the points projecting from the scales and the row of dark, air-filled spaces of the medulla.

2*c*. A hair from a reindeer. The bulk of the shaft consists of irregularly arranged air-filled medullary cells.

2*d*. A hair from a Persian gazelle. The large medullary cells have a more regular arrangement than in the reindeer and the very thin cortical layer and cuticle are visible at the sides.

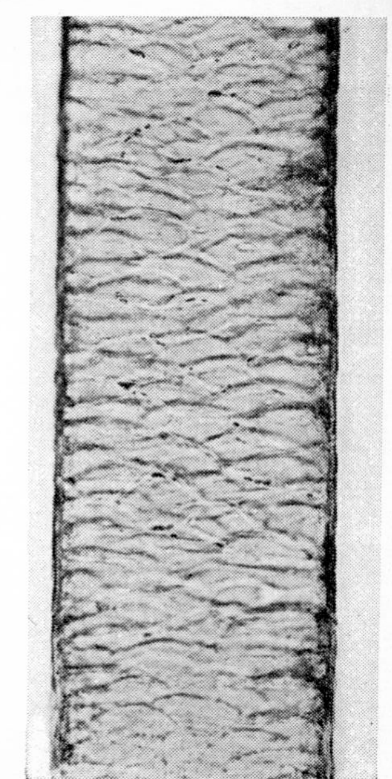

2*d*

3. Geographical variation (see p. 134).

persal range determined by the mobility of the pollen-carrying insects, which may themselves be ecologically limited.

The effectiveness of ecological specialization as an isolating agent need not necessarily be determined by the spatial segregation which it imposes upon the different populations. If divergence has reached a point where each population has achieved a high degree of adaptation to its particular habitat, any cross-breeding will tend to break up the favourable complexes of genes by bringing about recombination. Hybrids will be unfitted to survive simply because they are adapted to none of the available habitats, and accordingly they will be selectively eliminated. Since reproductive isolation here depends upon the relative inviability of hybrids, the situation is of the kind discussed below under (*e*). Isolation dependent upon the elimination of ill-adapted hybrids pre-supposes stringent selection in a severely competitive milieu, such as is experienced by the plant communities in mature forest associations. Convincing evidence of the prior existence of this type of ecological isolation may be seen wherever man has destroyed or opened up natural vegetation, so simultaneously eliminating old barriers and creating new habitats. The resulting 'de-isolation' permits freer cross-breeding of species previously separated ecologically, and the new habitats allow establishment of the hybrids without the pressure of competition. Complex populations of the kind known as hybrid swarms then arise, consisting of mixtures of first and later generation hybrids and 'backcrosses' between hybrids and parents, together with parental types.

(*b*) *Seasonal and temporal isolation*

Reproductive isolation dependent upon differences in the times of sexual maturation may, like ecological isolation, vary widely in efficiency, but in combination with some degree of habitat preference it can form a considerable barrier to miscegenation. The essential condition is that the peak periods of sexual activity should be sharply distinct in time, with little or no overlap. Where the breeding season is protracted, as with many higher vertebrates, this condition is not readily fulfilled, but with many invertebrates and plants with activity-cycles closely locked to the annual march of seasons the breeding period is brief and the opportunities for the evolution of systems of chronological isolation good. To be effective over a period of time, seasonal isolation of this kind must involve quite precise regulation of the times of reproductive activity. In many plants and animals, the regulation turns out to be dependent on the seasonal changes in length of day, a variable exclusively established by latitude and uninfluenced by minor local fluctuations in climate.

Diurnal, as well as seasonal, 'staggering' of reproductive activity can establish some measure of isolation, and this has recently been shown to be significant among wind-pollinated grasses. Of some sympatric species-pairs, one member releases pollen in the morning and the other in the evening, and the stigmas of each species are receptive only at the appropriate times, so considerably reducing the chances of receiving foreign pollen. Similar systems no doubt operate among insect pollinated plants, dependent upon times of pollen shedding and nectar flow, but these remain to be investigated.

(c) Isolation due to restriction of mating

In the animal case, restriction of breeding in its most elementary form involves simply a failure of illegitimate unions because of mechanical barriers to successful copulation, and in its most complex, a positive form of mate-selection, which may be a function of individuals or, as in the case of *apartheid*, of whole communities. Mechanical isolation has long been regarded as of considerable significance in insects, largely because closely allied species often show marked structural differences in their genitalia even when they are otherwise very similar. This fact cannot be without its evolutionary meaning, but in recent years there has been less inclination amongst entomologists to attach overwhelming significance to structural incompatibility of genitalia as species-separating barriers, since in many investigated examples the principal barrier has turned out to be what Darwin termed sexual aversion – a reluctance even to attempt copulation. Incompatibility of the latter type arises from a break-down at some point in the interlocking processes of recognition, stimulus, and response which lead up to coition in the more sentient animal groups; it is based upon differences in behaviour, and the reproductive segregation which it brings about is commonly called ethological isolation. Studies in the popular modern field of animal behaviour have indicated how complex may be the rituals of courtship, and how manifold the opportunities for the evolution of habit differences, and so of 'sexual aversion', in both invertebrates and vertebrates. Amongst invertebrates with rigid 'instincts', the courtship procedure may involve actions and responses which have the predictability of chemical reactions. Some indeed are of this very nature; thus in certain spiders, the mating reaction of the male is initiated by contact with a substance on the surface of the female; the substance can be extracted and shown to retain its stimulatory powers. It is a short step from this to recognition by scents – sometimes, as with the emperor moth, transmissible over remarkable distances – which plays so important a part in insects and mammals with highly developed olfactory senses. In other groups, recognition stimuli are received via different senses. Blair has shown that the calls of the males of various North American frogs are quite remarkably species-specific, and has used modern electronic equipment to analyse the differences in pitch, duration, and timbre, and to show that the occasional hybrids have calls of intermediate character. In birds, where the senses of sight and hearing are better developed than scent, songs and various visual stimuli are combined often in elaborate manner in the courtship which precedes mating. Some of the characteristics attributed by Darwin to sexual selection, which he supposed were evolved as a result of 'a struggle between the individuals of one sex, generally the males, for possession of the other', are now better to be understood as species-specific recognition characteristics which aid mate-selection and thus contribute to reproductive isolation.

The highest level of organization is to be seen among mammals, where conditioning plays a role. In the human race, psychological factors predominate in the immediate process of mate-selection in most advanced societies, although the circle of potential mates may be very severely limited by other influences. The differentiation of the human races took place under the protection of geographical isolation – isolation now no longer fully effective because of the increase of populations and the improvement in means of transport. Today, a multitude of factors, as diverse as religion and radio advertising, are interacting in different parts of the world to determine whether racial distinctions shall be perpetuated, or eroded by interbreeding.

Comparable phenomena in plants to ethological isolation in animals have been less investigated, but they do exist. Perhaps selective fertilization due to directed movement of spermatozoa in response to specific substances diffusing from the eggs – which may well play an important part as a species isolating mechanism in seaweeds where fertilization takes place in water after the mass release of eggs and sperms – should be excluded from the class of 'ethological' isolating systems; although whether a line can justifiably be drawn between responses to water-borne 'scents' like this and the unconditioned reflex reactions to air-borne scents which govern the mating behaviour of many insects is doubtful. In the higher plants, the evolution of pollinating systems dependent upon the collaboration of insects has permitted the development of systems of isolation based upon variation of the structure, colours, patterns, and scents of flowers. Conrad Sprengel was the first botanist to recognize the role of the flower as an allaesthetic* organ, and his lead was followed by Darwin, who in the classical work reported in *Fertilization of Orchids* and *Forms of Flowers* demonstrated the role floral variation could play in determining breeding behaviour. To form an isolating mechanism, floral variation must be such that it establishes a non-random dispersal of pollen; this would obviously be achieved if visiting animal pollinators tended to

* *Allaesthetic* : a term introduced by Sir Julian Huxley for organs or structures which produce a biological effect by stimulating the sense organs of another organism.

specialize on particular types. A broad segregation is immediately provided by the specialization of flowers for different kinds of pollen vectors – bird, moth, bee, or other insect. The red and white campions – highly interfertile when crossed artificially – owe their independence in nature largely to the fact that the former is habitually pollinated by bees during the day, while the latter is visited by moths in the evening when its pure white flowers are conspicuous in the dusk. The more refined types of isolation involve selective visitation of pollinators, which, in a particular foraging run, tend to concentrate on a particular flower type, guiding their choice by the perception of subtle variations in colours, patterns, and scents. When one considers how important floral variation may thus be in establishing reproductive isolation – and so species limits – in insect-pollinated flowering plants, it is not surprising that the delimitation of taxonomic species in systematic texts should be based so much upon floral character: the systematist is only following the pollinator! There is an interesting analogy here with the use of characters of the genitalia as taxonomic criteria in some insect groups.

(*d*) *Failure of fertilization*

Successful copulation or pollen transfer does not guarantee the formation of a hybrid; fertilization has yet to follow, and the fertilized egg to develop. In animals with internal fertilization, the route from the point of entry to the egg must provide a suitable environment for the sperm, otherwise fusion cannot occur. Proof of this has come from experiments with birds, in which foreign sperm has been found to be inhibited rapidly after artificial introduction into female genital tracts if the relationship was not a close one. In plants, pollen, after receipt on the stigma, must germinate to produce a pollen tube, and the pollen tube must grow through the tissues of the style until it enters an ovule and discharges the male nuclei into the embryo-sac. All of these processes demand exact physico-chemical compatibility if fertilization is to be achieved. As a first bar to crossing in species pollinated by wind or undiscriminating insects, pollen-style incompatibility has a widespread significance as an isolating mechanism. Many remote crosses have not even a starting chance of success, since pollen grains burst or are entirely inhibited from germinating on the foreign stigma. In closer crosses, as Kostoff showed in a range of tobacco species, the growth of the foreign pollen tubes may be slower than normal, so that when a mixture of pollen reaches the stigma, hybrid unions are always the less probable.

There is an additional way in which pollen incompatibility can form a barrier to hybridization in flowering plants. The development of seeds and fruit is sometimes dependent upon the receipt of a pollen-borne stimulus which activates a growth hormone in the ovary. This stimulus is something independent of fertilization, but unless it is present, progeny cannot be produced. Its absence appears to be the cause of the intersterility of certain species of *Solanum*, since hybrids are produced when a substitute for the normal growth hormone is supplied at the time of pollination.

(*e*) *Isolation due to hybrid inviability or sterility*

Should fertilization be achieved, there remain several other tests of the functional compatibility of the nuclear and cytoplasmic materials donated by the two parents. The fertilized egg must develop into a normal embryo; the embryo must grow into a self-maintaining adult, and the adult must produce viable sex cells and itself reproduce.

Hybrid inviability may be due to a variety of causes, ranging from nuclear or cytoplasmic disharmony which may prevent even the first division of the egg, to subtle ecological maladjustments which, as we have seen, may prevent the establishment of the hybrid organism in any of the environments available to it. The developmental errors arising from genetic disharmony in hybrids are manifold. In the bulk of investigated cases lethality has not been traced to specific causes, but it is clear that a very common feature is the breakdown of growth regulation. In the tobacco genus this is seen in some interspecific crosses in the anomalous course of early cell divisions in the embryo; in other crosses it does not appear until late in ontogeny, when cancerous tumours develop on the stems. Less severe departures from normal growth in hybrids may, on the one hand, involve slower development and poorer growth co-ordination, or on the other, higher growth rates and seemingly enhanced vigour – the latter the phenomenon of heterosis, or hybrid vigour.

Hybrid sterility, also, may arise from many causes. In certain moth crosses, hybrids are inevitably incapable of breeding, since the regulation of sexuality is impaired to the extent that one or the other sex is absent or replaced by intersexes. In some instances this has been traced to the incompatibility of the hybrid nucleus of the egg with the mother-donated cytoplasm in which it starts life. Comparable phenomena are known in plants as in certain willow-herb crosses which produce male-sterile progeny.

But the most frequent cause of the infertility of inter-specific hybrids lies in their inability to form functional sex cells because of irregularities in the cell division (meiosis) at which the double (diploid) chromosome number of the body cells is reduced to the single (haploid) chromosome set of the sex cells. This may result from genetically determined defects in the division itself, or irregularities may arise from an incompatibility of the chromosome sets derived from the parents. In any event, the sex cells receive unbalanced chromosome complements and either immediately die, or, if capable of surviving themselves, are unable to contribute balanced and functional gene combinations when they come together at fertilization.

The origin of isolation : the theory of geographical speciation

Finding out how a particular isolating mechanism works is one thing, but arriving at an acceptable conclusion as to how it originated, quite another. In the first instance the matter is open to investigation through direct observation and experiment; in the second, we can only estimate probabilities by study of the context and by reference to analogy. Because authors have placed weight upon different types of interpretation, even within the same taxonomic group, this is a field which has seen a fair amount of controversy. However, it has now become very

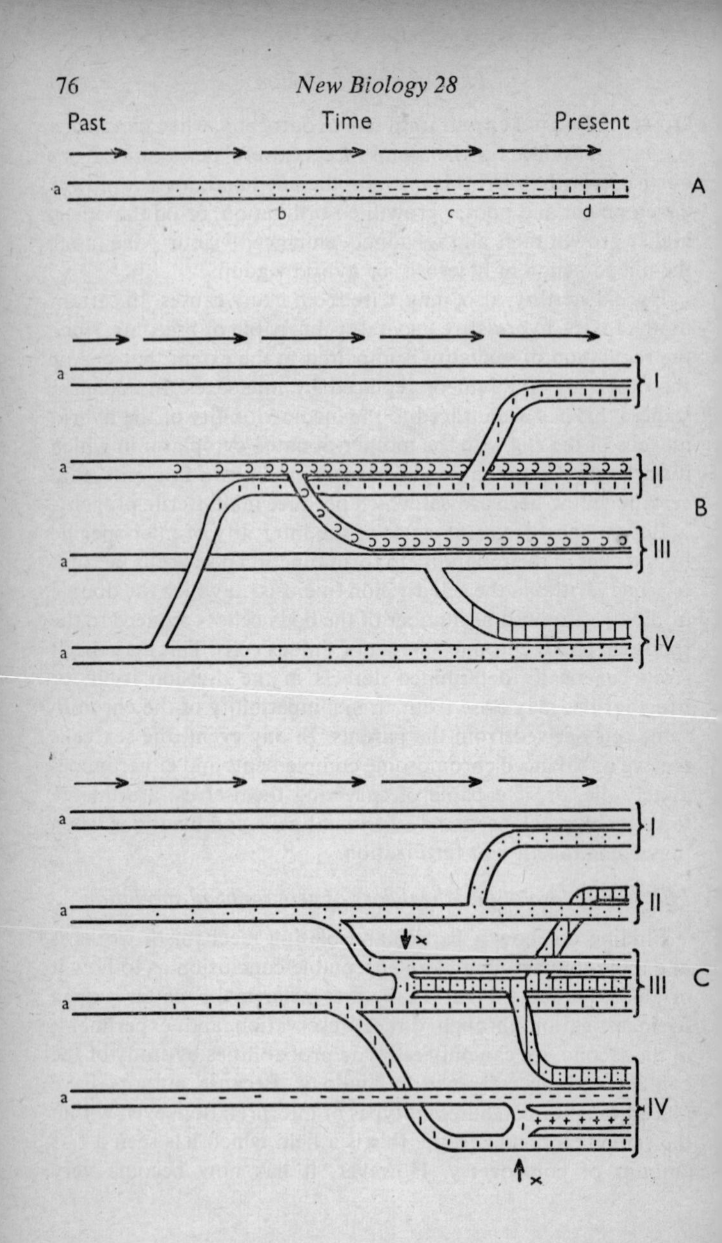

Past
Time
Present
a
b
c
d
A
a
I
a
II
B
a
III
a
IV
a
I
a
II
x
a
III
C
a
IV
x

widely accepted that among outbreeding sexual organisms, isolating mechanisms which do not now depend upon spatial isolation have often depended in the past upon such separation for their evolution. Sometimes the proposition is put more strongly – 'some degree of geographical isolation is an essential for species formation'; and the argument is even extended to assert that geographical isolation necessarily leads to speciation.

Darwin's contemporary, Moritz Wagner, was the principal early exponent of the view that geographical isolation is a prerequisite for diversification and so for species multiplication. Darwin accepted the point clearly enough; in a letter to Semper in 1878 he agreed that spatial separation of populations would greatly aid 'specification' (his own somewhat ambiguous precursor for our modern term 'speciation'). But in the same letter he stated that there are 'two different classes of cases ... viz., those in which a species becomes slowly modified in the same country ... and those cases in which a species splits into two or three or more new species'; only in the second situation could he agree that the origin of species was facilitated by isolation.

Fig. 1. Diagrams to illustrate different modes of speciation.

A. Evolution takes place by progressive change in a population in the same geographical region. The 'species', *a*, *b*, *c*, and *d*, follow each other in time, and are never co-existent.

B. An original species, *a*, becomes broken up into geographically isolated population, I–IV, in different regions. Some of the populations undergo evolutionary divergence until they are reproductively isolated. Further migration brings some of these new species back into contact with each other, but cross-breeding is no longer possible. Species formation in an archipelago like the Galápagos Islands can be interpreted in this manner.

C. Speciation following geographical isolation as in B, but with the additional process of polyploidy. At the points marked 'X' new species arise through the addition of the chromosome sets of pre-existing species; these new species may continue to co-exist with the parents, or may migrate outside of the area in which they originated. This has been the commonest pattern of evolution in higher plants.

The process of speciation based upon prior geographical isolation is illustrated diagrammatically in Fig. 1B, a development of one due to Mayr. The original population, spreading centrifugally as its numbers increase, becomes fragmented into spatially isolated sub-populations. As a result, what was formerly a single unit within which free interbreeding of individuals could take place becomes two units within which random mating might occur, but between which little or no gene exchange can take place. Each such breeding unit is now independent so far as its future evolution is concerned, and divergence may ensue as a result of differences in local selective pressures or even as an outcome of random change. If independence is maintained for a period long enough, it is presumed that genetical differences might become established which would lead to reproductive isolation even if the two populations came to occupy the same territory. After this critical event – the loss of the potentiality for interbreeding – should contact be established again, either by fresh migration across the barrier or by the disappearance of the barrier itself, then no longer would the two populations blend into one another as a result of miscegenation. Instead they would be capable of existence side by side without losing their identity, protected from hybridization by the inherent isolating mechanism. Constant repetition of this process at different rates and to varying degrees of completion may be expected to produce the pattern of partial and completely overlapping species areas which is a familiar characteristic of biogeography.

This, then, is the general picture; but like all generalizations it involves simplification. To begin with the processes leading to the fragmentation of originally continuous populations are diverse in themselves. The simplest process to envisage – that of the total separation of colonies of a widespread organism by the emergence of new topographical barriers like seas and mountain systems – has no doubt occurred repeatedly in the past, but has probably been of considerably less importance than the disintegration which may occur during the course of migration and colonization across a diverse terrain. It is to be expected that in the course of such an expansion of area both favourable and unfavourable habitats will be encountered; the favourable will sustain high numbers of individuals, the unfavourable, low. The outcome will be varying density of individuals across the whole terrain, with local concentrations separated from others by tracts bearing few individuals or none at all. Clearly gene exchange within these local concentrations will proceed more freely than between different ones, which will accordingly be partially, but not entirely, isolated. There is good reason to believe that this type of situation is a particularly significant one. An extreme example would be the colonization of an archipelago, where occasional random dispersal from island to island would serve to set up a series of colonies which would only be in breeding contact one with the next to the extent that further chance dispersal carried individuals across the intervening straits.

This reference to dispersal range directs attention to an important feature of spatial isolation – namely that the effectiveness of a barrier, be it topographical, climatic, or ecological, will vary from organism to organism according to the capacity of each to overcome it. This in general will depend upon the means of dispersal available to each species. We might expect to observe differences between, say, highly motile birds with great dispersal ranges, and plants in which the mature organism is fixed throughout its life to one spot, in the areas covered by individual breeding populations, and in the relative effectiveness of barriers like stretches of water or unsuitable terrain in circumscribing them. Such differences are indeed to be found. They can be observed even within the major groups; thus the spatial extent of breeding units in territorial birds (i.e. those in which each breeding pair stakes out its own territory) is less than in non-territorial, and in higher plants, where gene spread is restricted to the periods of pollen and seed dispersal, less in insect pollinated species than in wind pollinated.

It is also noteworthy that other intrinsic characteristics of the organism may decide the effectiveness of different types of extrinsic barriers – namely, those concerned with its habitat tolerances. This is obvious enough when extreme types are compared; thus the system of barriers operating within a country like Great Britain for an aquatic plant or a fresh-water fish is obviously totally different from that affecting a small mammal or a forest tree. However, even between closely related species, differences may exist which establish widely different population patterns in a single geographical area; consider for example the contrast between the house mouse and the field mouse, or between the two common species of campion mentioned above, the white campion, frequently an adventive or weed of cultivation, and the red campion, a plant of copses, woodland, and hedgebank.

In the foregoing discussion, geographical isolation has been treated as though it depended primarily upon the intervention of extrinsic barriers between breeding populations, barriers which effectively prevent or check gene flow because they are not crossed by adults, or by seeds, pollen, or other 'propagules'. There is, however, another possibility, namely that distance itself should act as an isolating factor even when the individuals of a species are fairly evenly and continuously dispersed in the intervening regions. Something like this situation must exist in every widely ranging species. An approach to truly random breeding can only occur within small populations of highly motile organisms, and where the total species area is substantially greater than the average dispersal range of the individual or its propagules, it will always be more probable that geographical neighbours will mate than individuals from the extremes of the distributional range. The essential point here is that whilst gene flow can occur throughout the species without the hindrance of extrinsic barriers, it is likely to be so slow between populations at different extremes of the range that they may be virtually independent of each other genetically and so capable of separate evolution.

Intrinsically determined barriers.

How, then do isolating mechanisms of other types develop once the way has been prepared for independent evolution in different populations by the establishment of geographical isolation? The diversity of isolating mechanisms should warn us against the assumption that any single principle can be deduced, but some of the main possibilities are clear enough.

Thus what may initially be 'geographical' isolation may pass by insensible steps into 'ecological'. Rarely will it be the case that the environmental conditions will be identical for every segment of a geographically fragmented species, and should they not be, then the various isolated populations will experience different selection pressures tending to bring them into closer harmony with the local environment. To begin with, this process might produce simply what the systematist calls a polytypic species, consisting of a sequence of subspecies each occupying a distinct geographical region and each somewhat different in ecology. Should two subspecies come into contact, much will depend upon how far their ecological divergence has progressed; if it has gone sufficiently far, it may be possible for them to co-exist in the same region without direct competition and without interbreeding. They would then, in effect, be 'biological species', sympatric, but held apart by ecological isolation.

In a study of one of the classical test cases of evolution, Darwin's finches of the Galápagos Islands, Lack has shown how a process like that just outlined is adequate to explain how it has come about that the different islands have become inhabited by groups of species, each exploiting a particular ecological niche, and each isolated ecologically as a result. According to Lack, the initial immigrants from the mainland of South America became dispersed over the group, and in partial geographical isolation the populations on the separate islands underwent divergent evolution in ecological character. Later migrations brought the different races into contact again; those which had diverged but slightly became reamalgamated, and those which differed sufficiently in ecology persisted side by side. This process, repeated a number of times, led to the present pattern of overlapping, ecologically specialized species and subspecies.

Processes of this type are clearly facilitated in an archipelago like the Galápagos where the different populations are partly but not completely isolated, and it is not surprising that his observations of the life of the Galápagos should have stimulated Darwin's imagination and caused him to open his first notebook on 'the transmutation of species' so early as 1837. But they have undoubtedly occurred in less diagrammatically lucid circumstances over areas of continental dimensions, although it sometimes requires a considerable effort for us now to withdraw sufficiently far from the local scene to appreciate this. It is amusing to note that even the pattern of speciation of lice is susceptible to the same type of explanation. Clay has recently shown that among lice infesting birds ecological specialization to head and body parts forms an isolating mechanism, and that it is highly probable that the ecological specialization which allows their 'sympatric' existence has developed in former isolation.

As we have seen, ecological isolation depends in the last analysis upon spatial segregation, and this may not prove a particularly efficient or permanent check upon miscegenation. Many of the other intrinsically determined forms of reproductive isolation are more efficient, and almost all are likely to be more permanent. It is important therefore to inquire how they might arise as an outcome of independent evolution in geographical isolation. As Darwin recognized, it is conceivable that they should develop simply as a by-product of evolutionary change, and this view has been elaborated by various modern geneticists, notably Muller. Within a normal breeding population, selection will necessarily favour the maintenance of an adequate level of fertility from generation to generation, irrespective of what other evolutionary changes may be progressing. Any severe divergence from the population mode in any phase of the reproductive process will be an 'abnormality' and liable accordingly to rejection. The modal behaviour itself may change in the course of time, however, either fortuitously or under selective pressure. Should such changes take place in isolated populations of a formerly continuous species, it does not follow that they will necessarily pursue the same course. So, in time, differences may accumulate sufficient to ensure that individuals of the different groups could not successfully interbreed, even if given the chance – in other words, they would become reproductively isolated. Almost any of the isolating mechanisms described above could be pictured as arising thus.

Now the essential feature of the process just outlined is not that selection favours the establishment of the isolating mechanism, but that in the absence of selection acting to maintain a harmonious balance in reproductive behaviour, geographically separate groups may drift apart and so become reproductively isolated fortuitously. We have, however, to consider the possibility that there may exist circumstances in which selection will actually favour the development and perfecting of an intrinsic isolating mechanism – not at all the same thing as favouring its maintenance once perfected.

This is a question which gave Darwin a good deal of intellectual difficulty. Since he recognized that racial divergence and so speciation depended upon the prevention of free interbreeding, he first considered it probable that inter-sterility might be acquired through natural selection. However, after contemplation of how this might have happened, he rejected the idea altogether, and concluded that the mutual infertility of species must have 'arisen incidentally during their slow formation in connexion with other and unknown changes in their organization' – that is to say, fortuitously, as a by-product of other evolutionary changes. The difficulty was that Darwin could not see how selection, which depends upon the differential reproduction of the variants composing a population, could possibly 'favour the survival of those individuals which happened to be endowed in a slightly higher degree with mutual infertility ...'. By adding a further stage to the argument, it is possible to see how selection could occasionally work in such a manner, at least to strengthen reproductive barriers between contiguous populations which have already undergone some adaptive divergence. Clearly there are no circumstances in which intersterility can be directly favoured, as such, between populations which are totally isolated spatially. But there are circumstances when spatial isolation is incomplete where two populations may be constantly influencing each other by occasional crossings. Now if each is adapted to its local habitat or mode of life, every crossing will produce a progeny less suited for survival than either parent since it will be relatively unadapted for either habitat. If all individuals are equally liable to crossing, then all will stand an equal chance of wasting progeny in this manner. On the other hand, if there are any individuals even slightly more likely to be fertilized by others from the same population than from the foreign one, they will be likely to leave a higher proportion of well-adapted offspring. Accordingly selection will favour the establishment of a barrier to interbreeding as such, since this will protect the adaptive gene complexes of the two populations.

That selection may act to reinforce an existing reproductive barrier has been demonstrated in an experiment by Koopman, using the fruit-fly, *Drosophila*. A mixed population of two species which occasionally hybridize to produce sterile progeny was maintained in a cage in which free mate-selection was possible. Females which accepted foreign males produced only sterile progeny; those which preferred their own species contributed normal fertile progeny to the next generation. In a comparatively few generations the tendency to accept a foreign mate was bred out of the mixed population, and the sexual isolation correspondingly perfected. It should be noted that this experiment casts no light on how the original sterility barrier arose, but it does illustrate the principle that selection can favour the development of certain types of isolating mechanisms when the progeny of crosses between contiguous populations is in some way defective or less well adapted to the available habitats. Should this be so, there is a number of interesting implications. One is that allied species from the same geographical region may be expected to show higher degrees of intersterility than those which have been long out of spatial contact, since in the latter case there can have been no premium upon an isolating mechanism as a means to facilitate independent evolution. That this is so was known to Darwin, and the fact itself may be taken as evidence that selection does function to establish isolating mechanisms. But it should not be forgotten that allied species cannot exist sympatrically at all without some reproductive isolation, so the logic of the argument is not quite so good as it seems.

Speciation without prior geographical isolation

In recent years there has been a good deal of debate about the possibility that reproductively isolated groups might arise from a parental stock without prior geographical isolation, i.e. that there might be sympatric as well as allopatric speciation. As we have seen, in Darwin's day Wagner urged that no such process was possible, and that all species formation depended upon prior isolation. Darwin found himself unable to agree with this extreme view, in part because he believed that ecological specialization in the one geographical region could permit local diversification.

The essential feature of sympatric speciation is that a single breeding group should become fragmented into two by the establishment of some inherent system of isolation, quite independently of the distribution of individuals. An early suggestion as to how this might happen was that in a variable population assortative mating – homogamy, or the pairing of like with like – might ultimately generate a number of independent breeding units and so prepare the way for sympatric race formation. This is one method used by breeders to produce pure-breeding strains after crossing, and in their hands it certainly produces results. Whether it ever happens in natural animal populations with sufficient persistency to have evolutionary effects is another matter. According to Mayr, the evidence that it does is exceedingly slight. Among insect-pollinated flowering plants the possibilities seem greater, as has been shown by Verne Grant and others. Homogamy here depends upon the flower constancy of pollinators, which, selecting a particular rewarding pattern of flower in a variable population of a given species, may concentrate upon it to the exclusion of others in a number of foraging flights, and so bring about pollination of like by like. In some large insect-pollinated groups like the orchids, there are genera where the distribution of species and the features in which they differ strongly indicate that diversification has resulted primarily from the activities of pollinators. In these genera new 'species' can in fact be synthesized by crossing existing species and assortative breeding of selected types from the progeny; but it would be difficult to provide any final proof that comparable processes have led to speciation in nature, and there will always remain the possibility that the different wild forms have evolved in former isolation.

'Instantaneous' sympatric speciation, resultant from a sudden change in the genetic system, is another matter, for here the evidence of the change remains, betraying unequivocally the story of its origin. The doubling of chromosome number which produces a polyploid is an example, for this is a sudden change which interposes a sterility barrier between parent and progeny. Rather more than half of all the flowering plants of the north temperate region have had this type of origin, so here polyploidy has been the principal method of speciation. Evidence accumulated by Professor Manton from the ferns shows that in the evolution of this ancient group polyploidy has been no less important. Speciation by polyploidy can happen either by the reduplication of the same set of chromosomes or the addition of different ones. The second event has been much more important than the first in the evolution of the flowering plants and ferns, and the chromosome sets which are added are generally derived from different species, or from different races of the same species which have already begun to diverge in their evolution – usually in geographical isolation. The combination of geographical race differentiation and polyploidy which has been so much a feature of plant evolution is illustrated in Fig. 1C.

As an evolutionary event, polyploidy is in a special category. By the sudden change in chromosome number the genetic balance is not seriously disturbed, and what effects are produced on the character of the plant are mostly of a quantitative nature. And yet, simultaneously with the establishment of the reproductive barrier, new evolutionary potentialities are opened up, not the least being the possibility of exploiting a state of permanent hybridity if the new polyploid has arisen from parents with different chromosome sets.

Apart from polyploidy, structural changes in the chromosomes arising accidentally in the course of nuclear division can fragment an originally continuous breeding population into separate breeding groups, by reducing the fertility of hybrids between individuals bearing the 'normal' and 'modified' chromosome types. Even minor chromosome changes, by restricting the amount of gene recombination possible in crossings between the original and modified forms, may serve to break up the species into groups with different genetic properties whilst not immediately lowering interfertility to any appreciable extent. Darlington in particular has stressed the widespread significance of these chromosomal changes as first steps towards speciation, and has expressed the view that changes establishing 'genetic isolation' have been more important than spatial isolation as causes of the origin of species.

Like polyploidy, structural change in the chromosomes is something which takes place in individuals, not simultaneously throughout whole populations. For these events to assume evolutionary significance, the changed type must be able to increase its numbers. Some authors, especially zoologists, have seen difficulties in this; Mayr, for example, regards it as improbable that new species should be founded by aberrant individuals of a parent species in more than a minority of cases. And yet there can be no doubt that this is just what has happened repeatedly in the evolution of plants, where it has been facilitated by circumstances perceived by Darwin – the static nature of plants, and their frequent hermaphroditism – circumstances which facilitate self-fertilization or very close inbreeding. In lower plant groups, single aberrant individuals can, through their capacity for asexual reproduction by spores, establish a respectably sized colony of a new type in a single generation. Among mosses and ferns with a hermaphrodite haploid generation, homozygosity can be reached in a single fertilization, and the new type then widely propagated by the ensuing spore-producing generation. In hermaphrodite flowering plants, the very circumstance of polyploidy may circumvent previous self-sterility and so allow self-fertilization and the immediate multiplication of the new type.

The successful establishment of a new reproductively isolated type as a species depends not only on its capacity for multiplication, but on its ability to survive. In a closely competitive society it will be pitted immediately against its own parental species; to become established, it must either displace the parents, or shift into an adjacent habitat. Success in either course would mean that the new type has, simultaneously with its achievement of reproductive isolation, gained some ecological potentiality lacking in its parents. That this could be so with a polyploid which has originated by the addition of different chromosome sets is obvious enough; the new state of permanent hybridity may offer advantages lacked by either parent. But it is not so easy to see how establishment could proceed in the face of rigorous competition if the new type were not endowed with some such new property. However, not all environments are so highly competitive that there is a strict one-for-one replacement of individuals from generation to generation. Especially among plants the largely fortuitous nature of dispersal and survival in open communities may permit the establishment of an aberrant form in appreciable numbers, as de Vries observed in his weedy populations of evening primroses. Sewall Wright has pointed out how chromosomal changes producing intersterility may spread by chance in populations which for some reason or other are fluctuating in numbers. During a phase of increase, a particular aberration could become established locally simply because it happened to be present in the small sample of individuals from which the colony arose.

But it is in the course of migration and the invasion of new habitats that chromosomal changes inhibiting gene recombination or establishing intersterility may assume their highest importance as factors determining the origin of species. Should the partly isolated breeding groups accumulate gene changes affecting ecological tolerance, they may be differentially selected in different parts of the species area. Spatial segregation and ecological pressures would then co-operate with the pre-existing factors contributing to internal discontinuity to fragment the original species, and, as we have seen, selection could force the process to completion so that the one species became several.

The evolutionary significance of isolation

What, then, is the significance of isolation in evolution? In so far as the biological species is determined by the barriers to free interbreeding which encompass it, the origin of species is the origin of reproductive isolation. But is speciation an inevitable part of evolution? In the passage from the letter to Semper quoted above, Darwin provided part of the answer to this question; one form of evolution, that involving continuous change in a single lineage, is not necessarily dependent upon isolation. Nevertheless, what has been termed *schistic* evolution has also been important, leading to a continuous diversification and multiplication of species. Something like 4,000,000 species exist on earth today, and Cailleux has calculated that perhaps 150,000,000 have existed in the whole history of life. What is the meaning of this staggering diversity?

Again Darwin produced an answer. 'The advantage of diversification of structure in the inhabitants of the same region', he wrote in the *Origin*, 'is, in fact, the same as that of the physiological division of labour in the regions of the same individual body.... No physiologist doubts that a stomach adapted to digest vegetable matter alone, or flesh alone, draws more nutrient from these substances. So in the economy of any land, the more widely and perfectly the animals and plants are diversified for different habits of life, so will a greater number of individuals be capable there of supporting themselves.' The argument can be taken a good deal further. A balanced economy of life on earth demands that living organisms should be diverse in their methods of exploiting the environment. Terrestrial life depends upon the utilization of solar energy and the continuous circulation of carbon, hydrogen, oxygen, nitrogen, and the other elements of which living things are composed; plant, animal, and micro-organism are complementary in these processes. As an imaginative exercise, it is possible to conceive of a protean type of life accomplishing in itself all of the anabolic and catabolic processes necessary for perpetual existence on earth, but such a life form would necessitate a type of physiology very different from anything which has so far arisen in the course of evolution. Perhaps only man could assume such omnipotence that he could dispense with the co-operation of other organisms in his life on earth, but even he might find it difficult to find a substitute for his own internal symbionts.

Diversification of function is thus an inevitable requirement for the persistence of life on earth. As Darwin saw, diversity of function implies specialization. For an evolving lineage to become specialized, it must be free from the disruptive effects of genetic contamination with others. In an asexual organism this is ensured since there is no sexual process to allow genetic contamination. But, by the same token, asexual lineages are debarred from rapid evolution; each, as it were, must make all its own inventions since there is no system whereby they can be pooled. Sexual reproduction provides such a mechanism in allowing gene-recombination; but while facilitating evolutionary change in this way, if unlimited in its scope it would inhibit diversification by randomizing the 'gene pool' in each generation. Isolation provides the antidote, by allowing the dissection of the gene pool into independent parts from time to time.

Thus isolation is a necessary adjunct to sexual reproduction if that specialization for differing modes of life, which Darwin recognized as a central feature of evolution, is to be attained. In this respect, evolution as it has progressed on earth has inevitably meant the origin of species. But the figure of 150,000,000 remains an arresting one; it suggests a lavishness beyond all reason – an element of diversification simply for the sake of diversification. Biologists whose work brings them into contact with the minutiae of specific differences are often impressed with their apparent non-adaptive character; and while there are many evolutionists prepared to perform the act of faith of asserting that all differences must be adaptive, a majority would no doubt agree with Sir Julian Huxley's judgement that much speciation has been 'a biological luxury, without bearing upon the major and continuing trends of the evolutionary process'.

FOR FURTHER READING

Dobzhansky, T. 1956. *Genetics and the Origin of Species.* New York.
Huxley, J. (Editor) 1940. *The New Systematics.* Oxford.
Huxley, J. 1942. *Evolution: The Modern Synthesis.* London.
Huxley, J., Hardy, A. C., and Ford, E. B. (Editors) 1954. *Evolution as a Process.* London.
Jepsen, G. L., Mayr, E., and Simpson, G. G. (Editors) 1949. *Genetics, Palaeontology and Evolution.* Princeton.
Mayr, E. 1942. *Systematics and the Origin of Species.* New York.
Stebbins, G. L. 1950. *Variation and Evolution in Plants.* Oxford.

AUTOMATIC MECHANICAL SELF-REPRODUCTION*

L. S. PENROSE

PERHAPS the most remarkable feature of living matter, as opposed to inanimate nature, is the power of self-reproduction. The property is so characteristic that Oparin (1957), perhaps the greatest authority on the origin of life, considers that life can be said to have arisen only after the evolution or emergence of this property. Before self-reproduction began there were conglomerations in the primordial soup, which is supposed to have once existed on the earth, but no life. Crystals, indeed, grow; and each part may be thought of as copying an earlier model. The parts are not differentiated, however, and there is usually no natural division into sections. So Schrödinger (1944) considered life to be an aperiodic crystal, that is to say, one which, by its nature, terminates in space, thus producing discrete organisms.

At this point we may recall another principle, or rule, adumbrated by William Harvey in his phrase 'omne vivum ex ovo', which, in its more modern form, says 'no life except from life'. The reaction of self-reproduction does not arise except from a seed of the same kind. Crystals can be started by a multitude of different kinds of seeds. A living substance, however, must not be able to arise except from its own seed. In extremely unusual circumstances it may arise as a consequence of some event akin to mutation.

There is another fundamental idea, which seems to follow from these principles, and it is genetical. If a change takes place in existing hereditary material, that is to say, a mutation, the changed state is repeated subsequently, not the original pattern.

* A public lecture given at University College London on 14 January 1958. (Drawings executed by A. J. Lee.)

There may be other basic principles, but there is something to be said for an attempt to find out how far a mechanical organism which had just these properties would progress.

The most characteristic property, that of self-replication, has been studied theoretically by certain mathematicians. The matter was summarized by Haldane (1954) in these words: 'Can one give a machine an instruction to make another one like itself also provided with a copy of these instructions? If so, as long as the parts needed to construct another such machine are available, the machine will go on reproducing its like, and so will its progeny. Von Neumann (1951), on the basis of a theorem due to Turing, claims to have proved that such a machine can be constructed from a finite number of parts of about twelve different kinds. If he is right, such a machine would have a considerable claim to be alive, even if it had to wander about hunting for ready-made Meccano parts as we have to wander about hunting for ready-made amino-acids and vitamins, as well as foodstuffs which are merely energy sources.'

No one was able to estimate the minimal total number of parts which would form such a machine, but this was generally believed to be great. The analogy of large molecules, such as proteins, obviously biased the estimate and the idea of actually constructing such an automaton seemed, for practical purposes, unattainable.

For many years I have been interested in such problems and I have often thought that the solution may be much more approachable than might be, at first glance, imagined. Some simple, everyday forms of pseudo-crystals are quite familiar, such as the zip fastener. This object assembles a series of pairs of units, provided that a start has been made on the pairing process. Other, more complex, repeating objects occur in such circumstances as photography, printing and in mass production from moulds. To reproduce mechanically an object of a complicated nature, the usual plan is to form a negative, or templet, on which new positives can be stamped. The method is uneconomical because the templet has no place in the finally assembled object. It is also extremely difficult to imagine how a self-reproducing system, involving a templet, can be made fully automatic.

The deliberate construction of self-reproducing objects is, I believe, a very recent development, less than one year old. It happened that my colleague, Roger Penrose, mentioned that, in his view, self-replication might theoretically be achieved by a set of objects containing magnets whose mutual attractions were altered when they were built up into specified shapes. The idea was sketched in this way. If such pieces were shaken up randomly in a liquid of the same density, or even in a sack or other enclosure, it would be so planned that they would not combine

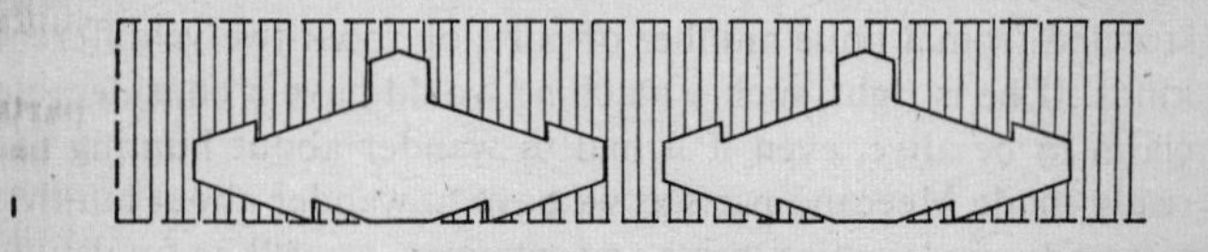

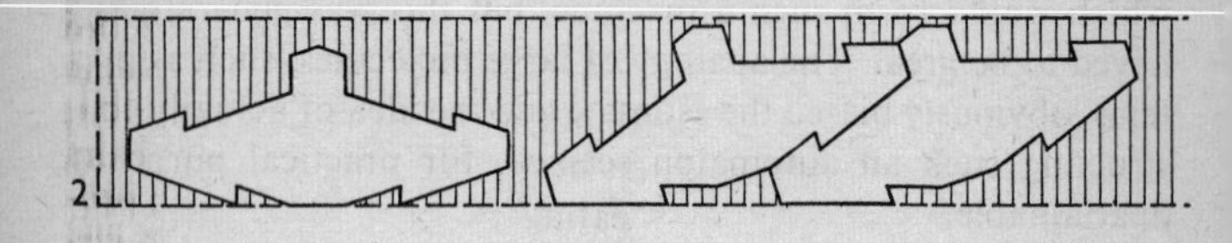

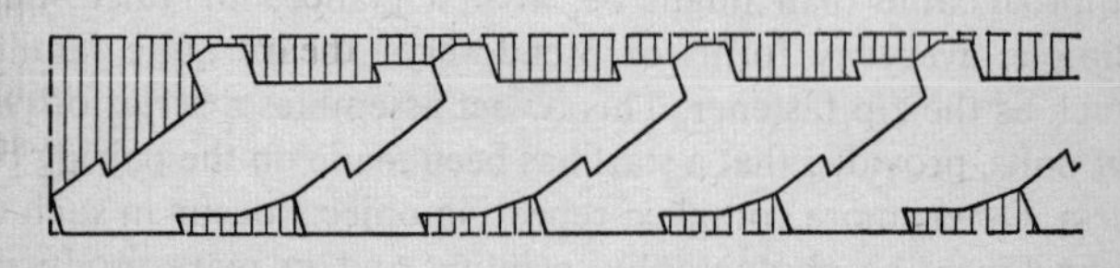

Fig. 1. Seeded Crystal.

1. Elements in neutral position; they do not link up when agitated horizontally.
2. A neutral element close to a linked pair.
3. The linked pair collects elements from both sides and forms a continuous 'crystalline' chain.

with one another; however, they might combine if they were seeded with a group put together to form a specified pattern. After an indefinite time, new examples of the seeded specified pattern should be formed. It occurred to me that there were practical possibilities here, but that magnetism was an awkward property to use; springs seemed likely to be more suitable but cumbersome. I suggested substituting gravity for magnetism. After many hours of discussion and trial drawings, we found that elements of a certain shape would coalesce like a crystal when shaken horizontally on a track. The restriction to one dimension, in place of three originally desired, was a serious concession, justified by the expedient of trying to bring about the most favourable conditions for making a start.

A fair-sized model was rapidly constructed out of plywood, as indicated in Fig. 1, and I was quite surprised to find that the idea actually worked. When seeded with material consisting of a complex of two linked pieces, a whole row of independent elements quickly copied them and became a connected chain under the influence of horizontal shaking. This result was obtained because the tilt which characterized a linked pair promoted further linking. There were, moreover, two different ways of starting this reaction, two phases or programmes, because the first pair can lean to the right or to the left. Two different kinds of artificial crystal can be produced from one kind of element.

The next step was to make this crystal aperiodic according to the theory of Schrödinger. This turned out to be very easy because it merely involved dispensing with some of the notches used for hooking the elements together in the crystal formation. Two kinds of basic units were used, complementary to one another. A model with such elements was described in a letter to *Nature*. When the pieces are randomly arranged and shaken in the track provided, they give rise to a phenomenon which is described in detail in Fig. 2. They only link up if the track is seeded with a linked complex. There is some doubt as to what precise conditions von Neumann had in mind for his automaton, but it seems that this model does provide an actual solution to his problem. Here we need only two sorts of unit; and one of

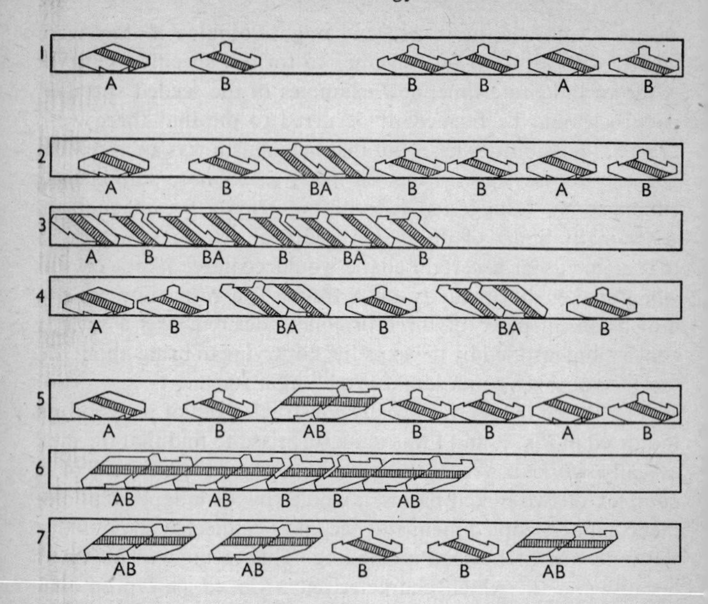

Fig. 2. Model to show self-replication, made with two types of unit, A and B.

1. Six units are placed on the track which is then shaken for a period; the units do not link.
2. Two linked units, BA, are now introduced; the shaking is resumed.
3. Now the effect of horizontal shaking is to produce conglomerations.
4. As shaking gradually stops the units separate again, but the old linked pair, BA, remains and a second linked pair has been generated.
5. At stage 2 two differently linked units, AB, are introduced.
6. Conglomeration produced by horizontal shaking.
7. After separation two new pairs AB are seen to have been generated.

each sort, when linked together, make a self-reproducing complex. It was found later that, in general, only one kind of unit was necessary for solution of the problem, as shown in Fig. 7, for example.

On detailed examination of the phenomenon, we observe that, in the absence of an activated complex, the material behaves as dead matter. However, exceptionally violent or unusual disturbance might spontaneously lead to the formation of a connected group. Moreover, two complementary phases of activation, analogous to two different mutations, are possible. Whichever one is used as a seed it will propagate its own kind.

Then there is the question of energy. Von Neumann is said to have proposed that the automaton could be supplied with unlimited energy. Here, shaking may be compared with the effect of heat or perhaps even with Brownian movement. The energy supplied is non-specific and kinetic, but the result is to produce structures which have potential energy by virtue of their use of hooks or ratchets; they trap energy in this way. This is probably a fundamental feature of living processes, the translation of kinetic energy into structure.

And what should be said about the track in which the pieces move? Besides supplying energy to the particles by collisions with its ends, and by friction, it restricts movement to one line. If they had the whole surface of a flat plane to move about on, pieces built with the same vertical section as those in Fig. 2, but about as thick as they were long, would occasionally get into the right position for replication. The narrow track greatly facilitates the right type of collision: indeed it makes it inevitable. Thus the track is like a chemical catalyst, in particular, a coenzyme. In these models the device ensures reproduction within a reasonable period of time.

It would be an important theoretical improvement if the ends of the track were dispensed with and friction alone relied upon to transfer energy from the moving track to the pieces. Moreover, it is possible to arrange for activated complexes, with ability to touch the roof of the track, to pick up energy not available to units in neutral position. In practice it is convenient to attach some spongy substance to the roof of the track at several different places. The effect of this is to transfer to the complexes themselves the function assigned, in the first instance, to the ends of the track. Indeed, one of the two activated complexes might be designed so as to pick up more energy than the other, thereby conferring upon it a relative selective advantage, enabling it to surpass the other in quantity of offspring produced in an endless track, where both types were present.

I had difficulty in finding a suitable name for the activated complexes produced in these experiments. On showing one of them to Professor A. J. Ayer, I inquired whether it perhaps might be a 'drogulus', a creature he had named in philosophical argument. He replied that it was undoubtedly a 'drogulus'; and the name seems very suitable since such terms as 'eobiont' or 'parabiont' have already been booked. In agreement with scientific terminology it could be a 'synapton' and its successful reproduction should, according to Mr N. W. Pirie, be called 'morphopoesis'. It could simply be called a 'zygote', if we like to think in genetical terms.

With the first models there are only two possible variations. It is natural to inquire whether an object containing more pieces and more variations can be constructed, using similar principles. If the units themselves are deformable, that is, if they have mobile parts, the number of possible positions they can take up, when locked together with others, can be indefinitely increased. By trial and error methods I found that the simplest method of obtaining increased variety was to add similar elements together laterally. In the first models of this type, each unit was multiple, as shown in Fig. 3. Here a three-fold (trimeric) complex has just reproduced.

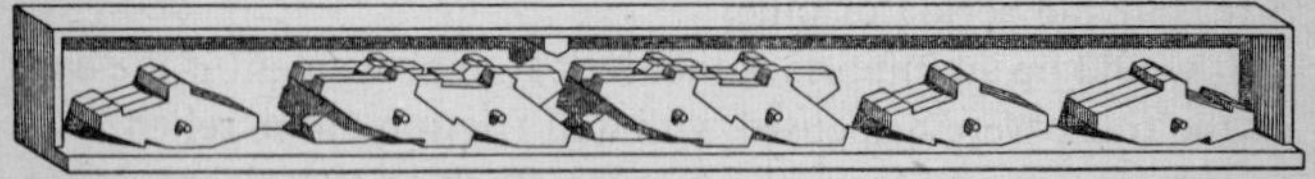

Fig. 3. Self-reproducing multiple complex.
Three-fold elements of two kinds, one the mirror image of the other, form self-reproducing complexes. There are eight possible alternative objects which can be used as seeds.

Later on, it was found possible to build complexes laterally from separate pieces, that is, to polymerize them, by a process akin to the basic method of linear crystallization. A polymeric synapton could feed upon strings of neutral, unactivated material. These neutral strands were prearranged only in that they consisted of elements tied together laterally. The question then arose as to how a newly-formed activated group could be disentangled from the unactivated, neutral, matrix of crystalline threads without untying itself at the same time. To achieve this some device was needed so that a neutral and a sensitized unit would not link up laterally to an activated unit, whether it was tilted one way (+) or the other way (–) although, if adjacent units were both neutral or both activated, they would stay together. An elementary form of such a link was easily developed and the result was interesting. It showed how a structure with (+) and (–) tilts and of any given length could, as it were, be cut out of a neutral matrix at any point where the matrix was, by chance, suitably orientated. The strands from which the neutral matrix is formed must be indefinitely long. It is as though a fly meeting a spider's web formed a new fly out of the web; a big surprise for the spider. In Fig. 4 the process is shown diagrammatically. A complex, made of five pairs of units laterally, cuts out a new replica from polymeric strands of neutral units. In this development, the total complex consists of 2N separate pieces and each pair can have two distinct forms. The complex can be used to carry a kind of Morse code of (+) and (–) tilts. As some people would say, each pair of elements carries one bit of information and so the whole complex carries N bits of information. Consequently a coded message of any length could be carried by such an object, the only practical limitation being the number of units, molecules, or 'haptons', available for their construction.

We have not considered how the possession of such a code, or programme, could be of benefit to the complex which carried it. How could one arrangement be better than another? Several answers can be given:

(i) The possession of a particular code enables the complex

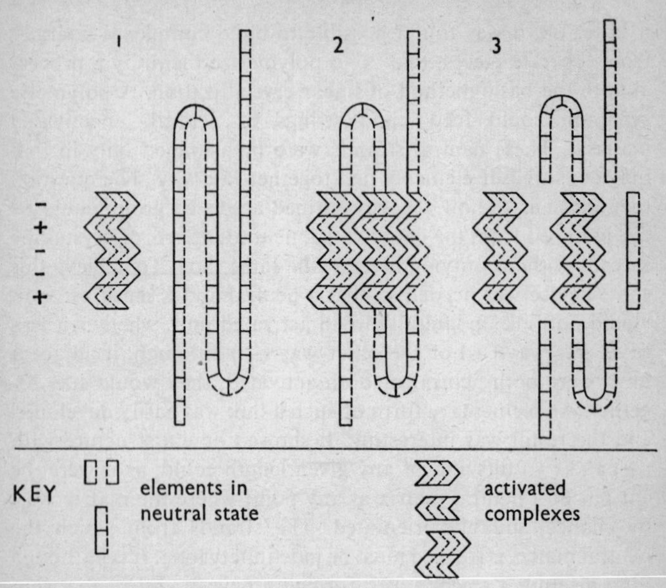

Fig. 4. Self-replication of a five-fold complex.

The food consists of strands of semi-crystalline neutral material.

1 A complex consisting of five pairs of elements, with tilts indicated by – and + signs, approaches a string of elements each in neutral state.

2 Sections of three adjacent strands are activated. Those suitably orientated have formed a new complex. Activated elements have become detached from neutral strands.

3 The complexes separate from the neutral material and from solitary strands temporarily activated.

to obtain energy from its surroundings by unlocking sources of power in the neighbourhood.

(ii) The code enables fresh supplies of units to be assembled or obtained ready made. The simplest method would be for the code to act as a kind of filter which let through food required for further reproduction and excluded other elements.

(iii) One advantage of some arrangements over others could

be that they are associated with greater structural stability or adaptability.

(iv) Some codes might enable a shield or skin to be formed around the complex to prevent it from being disorganized by blows caused by chance encounters with stray, unwanted elements. Allied to this is (v) the necessity of extending its track, or living space, and guiding new units into the most useful path.

All these things could be performed by a code if the environment contained sources of power and food, locked up or inaccessible without this key. A fanciful representation of such a source is given in Fig. 5. We suppose that such charged objects occur naturally at intervals along a shaking track. When hit by an activated complex with the right code, they are unlocked. A plunger, then released, hooks on to the floor of the moving track and a shower of food is delivered. The object itself, when emptied, moreover, provides some external protection.

This analogy, though crude, leads to an interesting idea. There are two ways in which the whole, or part of, a synapton might arise spontaneously. The first way is by some very unusual kind of shaking; this way is analogous to gene mutation. The second way is by collision of unactivated elements with some peculiar object in the vicinity. Then the code carried by the synapton could have been formed initially by collision with its environment. If a discharged object was the original cause of the shape of the key, this would be very favourable for the synapton's survival. The formation of adaptive enzymes by bacteria and in our own everyday production of antibodies to deal with innumerable foreign particles are perhaps complex processes of this character. It seems possible that, during the course of early evolution of cells, the necessary variation produced by mutation was delegated to the nucleus, while the second type of variation, replicated change in response to environment, was delegated to the cell cytoplasm.

The complexes so far described have had the property of forming new ones without disturbing the originals from which the copies are made. The effect of hooking together desensitizes the ends of the complexes, preventing them from joining any-

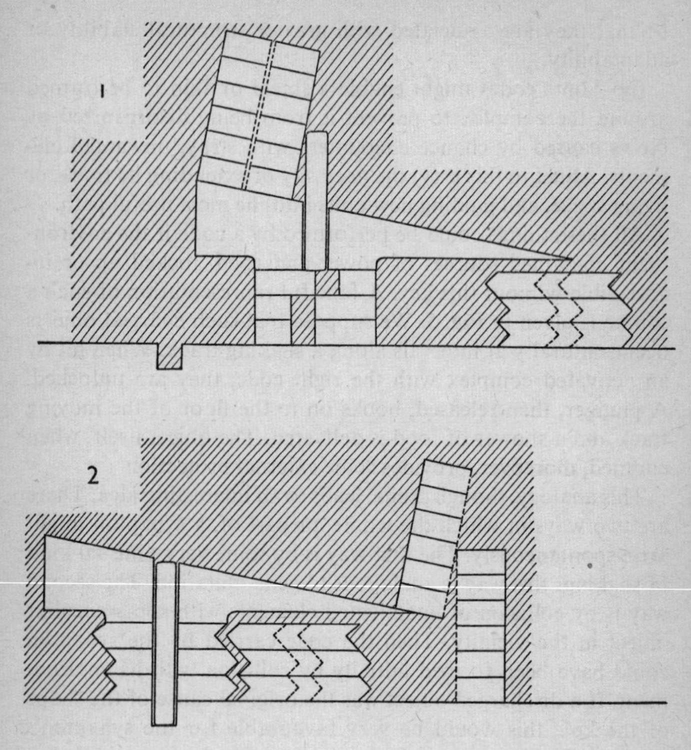

Fig. 5. Fanciful representation of natural source of food.
1 Charged group of elements and activated complex with special programme.
2 Group unlocked and discharged by activated complex; new material is released for reproduction of the complex and extra energy provided by attachment to the track.

thing else. Let us plan that it shall do more than this and arrange that junction of two pieces also releases previous connexions. A new and more adaptable reproductive system results, and it needs some explanation. Its basic food need consist of only one kind of unit, but this must contain elements capable of activation at two levels. The lower level, as before, induces linking with the next element, but the higher level induces release.

This new property is explained diagrammatically in Fig. 6, using elements with sliding levers. As before, two elements in neutral position do not link up. If two elements are linked, the first is at a low level of activation but the second, by virtue of its link to the first, is activated at a higher level and released from any element to which it was previously hooked, as in Fig. 6 (i) 2. If another neutral element moves into contact with the first complex, as shown in Fig. 6 (i) 3, it will hook on to the left-hand unit and will push it into the high level position previously held by its partner and this will release the partner at the same time. The new complex, in Fig. 6 (i) 4, has exactly the same form as the previous one. By feeding successive elements to the left of the complex, the group will be destroyed and renewed simultaneously, demonstrating a steady state but no reproduction. There is still only one complex, engaged in a process akin to metabolic and katabolic flow so characteristic of living organisms; there is assimilation and excretion of elements without change of structure.

Though it is able to feed, this type of complex does not reproduce itself. However, the basic units can be made dimeric, that is, they can consist of elements tied together laterally in pairs. When this is done, the total 'live' complex consists of two dimeric units and feeding the live complex with neutral dimeric units can lead to self-reproduction. To achieve this end, the activation of the laterally attached elements must be in opposite directions, as shown in Fig. 6 (ii) 1. Using the rule demonstrated in Fig. 6 (i) 2 and 3, we can work out what happens when a dimeric unit is added. The result, shown in Fig. 6 (ii) 2, is a complex formed from three activated units. The released elements cannot escape because they are tied laterally to linked elements. Addition of a fourth unit (Fig. 6 (ii) 3) completely releases the two central hooks and the two live complexes separate. In fact, they repel one another as the two released, but not detached, elements fall to their lower level of activation and, in doing so, hook on to their neighbours. The two new synaptons are solidi-

(i)

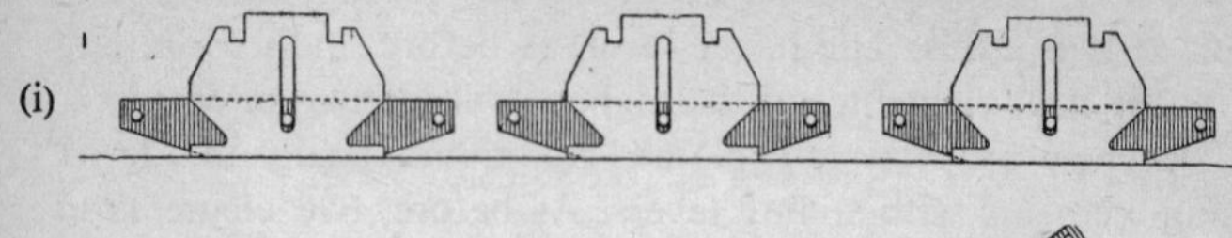

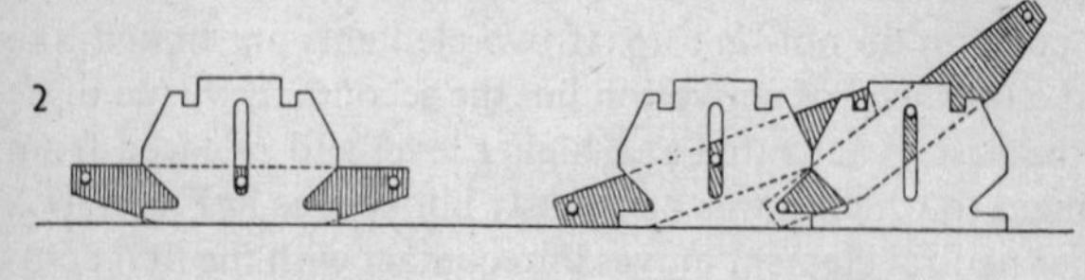

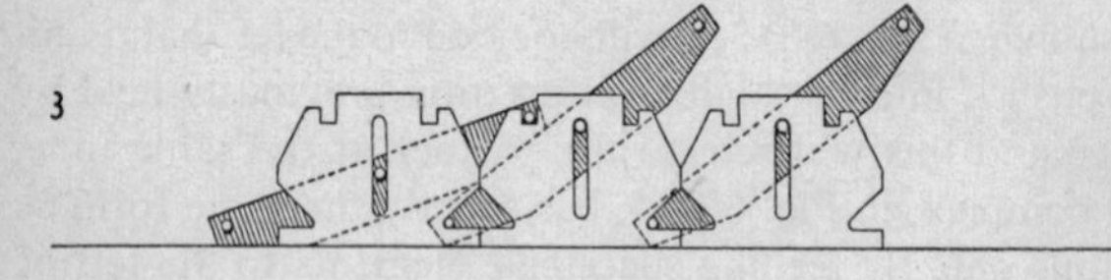

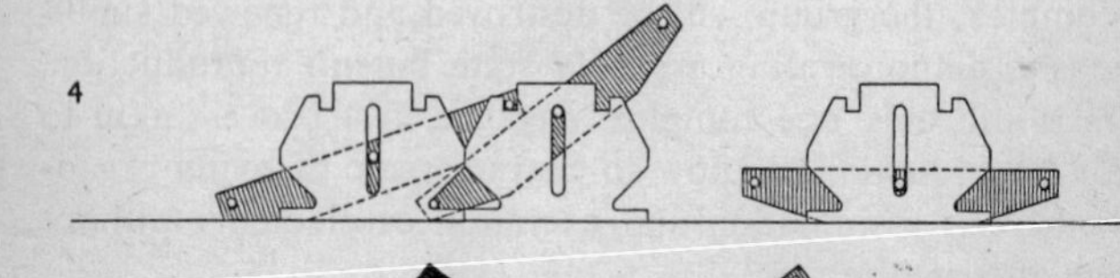

(ii)

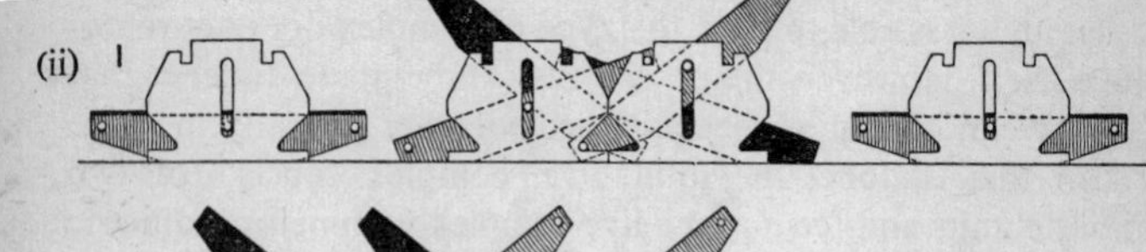

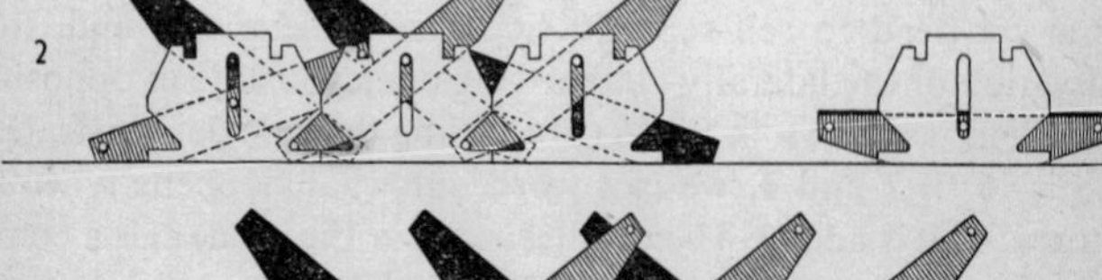

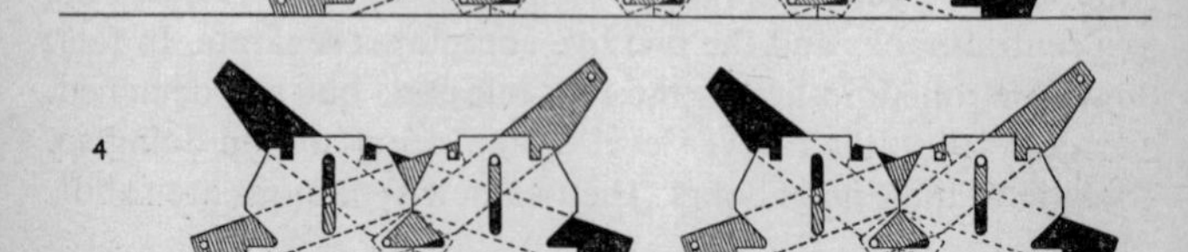

fied after local agitation. The final result is shown in Fig. 6 (ii) 4.

In the actual construction of models, it is convenient mechanically to attach two elements together firmly. The moving parts, or levers, can slide on some kind of vertical axis, as shown in Fig. 7. In Fig. 8 the whole action is shown diagrammatically, as though from above. We note that, in Fig. 6 (ii) 2 and in Fig. 8 (ii) 3, the group of three units is symmetrical. It is thus immaterial whether the fourth unit is added on the right or the left side. When both new units come in from the same side, the original complex is repeated in a manner similar to that described in Fig. 2; but when the new units are added from opposite sides the original complex breaks and loses its identity in reproduction. This type of replication, in which the parent's identity is lost, is strongly reminiscent of mitotic cell division.

By suitable devices it has been found possible to differentiate mechanically between these two types of reproduction so that, for instance, a given synapton is obliged to divide every time it reproduces. Another development is to form polymeric chains

---

Fig. 6. Diagrammatic exposition of reproduction based on a steady state principle.

(i) 1. Three elements with sliding levers and pins in neutral position: they do not link up.
2. One neutral and two linked elements: that on the right is doubly activated.
3. The third element approaches on the left and becomes attached. The new element, linked with the left part of the activated complex, causes this to be doubly activated thereby releasing its former partner. The complex retains its structure though made of different elements.
4. The released element sinks to its neutral state.

(ii) 1. If each unit consists of two elements, a pair of units can form a stable activated complex.
2. A triple complex has been formed by adding a dimeric unit.
3. Yet another unit has been added. The four-fold unstable complex so formed is ready to separate.
4. Duplication is achieved after all levers have dropped to their lowest possible levels.

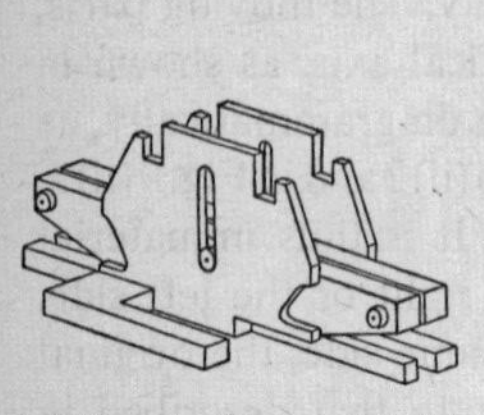

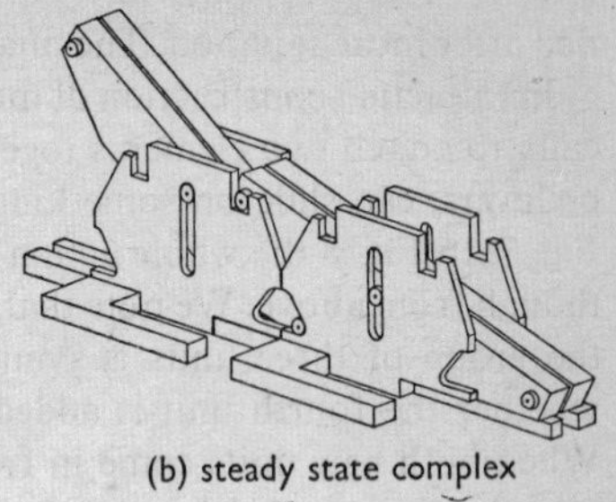

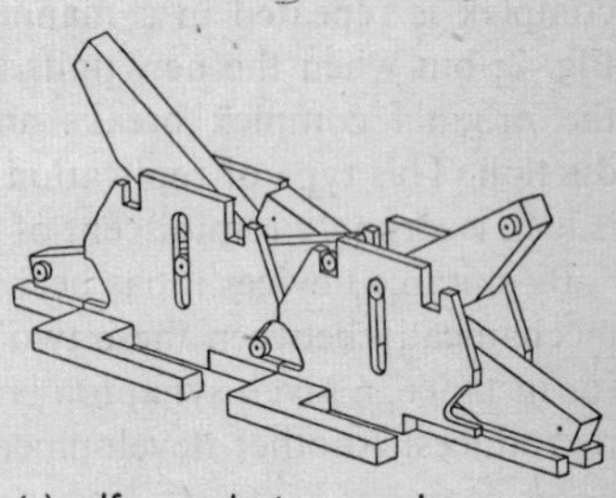

Fig. 7. Exact drawings of working models.
(a) Dimeric unit in neutral phase.
(b) Activated complex which maintains its steady state when fed with neutral units.
(c) Activated complex which reproduces itself when fed with neutral units. The lateral hooks indicate how a chain of such complexes can be constructed.

as with forms described earlier. Fig. 9 indicates how the principle of feeding from semi-crystalline chains of natural elements can be applied to this type of reproduction. Here the synapton is five-fold instead of being two-fold, as in Fig.8. The arrangement of (+) and (−) tilting could theoretically be extended indefinitely in this manner.

Some people object to these models because, they say, this is not how desoxyribosenucleic acid (DNA), the chief component of cell nuclei, replicates itself. The answer is that it is not the intention to show how DNA replicates. The models show how

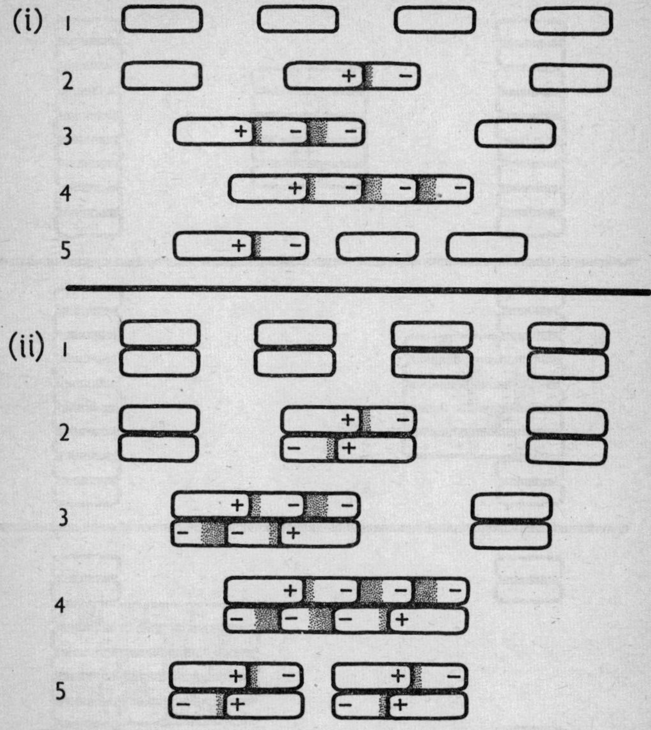

Fig. 8. Alternative diagram of reproduction based on a steady state principle.

(i) 1. Neutral food elements.

2. Steady state complex added.

3, 4, and 5. The complex picks up food from its left; it releases and ultimately repels elements on its right.

(ii) 1. Dimeric neutral food units.

2. Live complex added.

3. The complex absorbs a unit from one side and forms a group of three.

4. A fourth unit is absorbed and an unstable group of four is produced.

5. The unstable complex breaks down into two pairs each of the same form as the original complex.

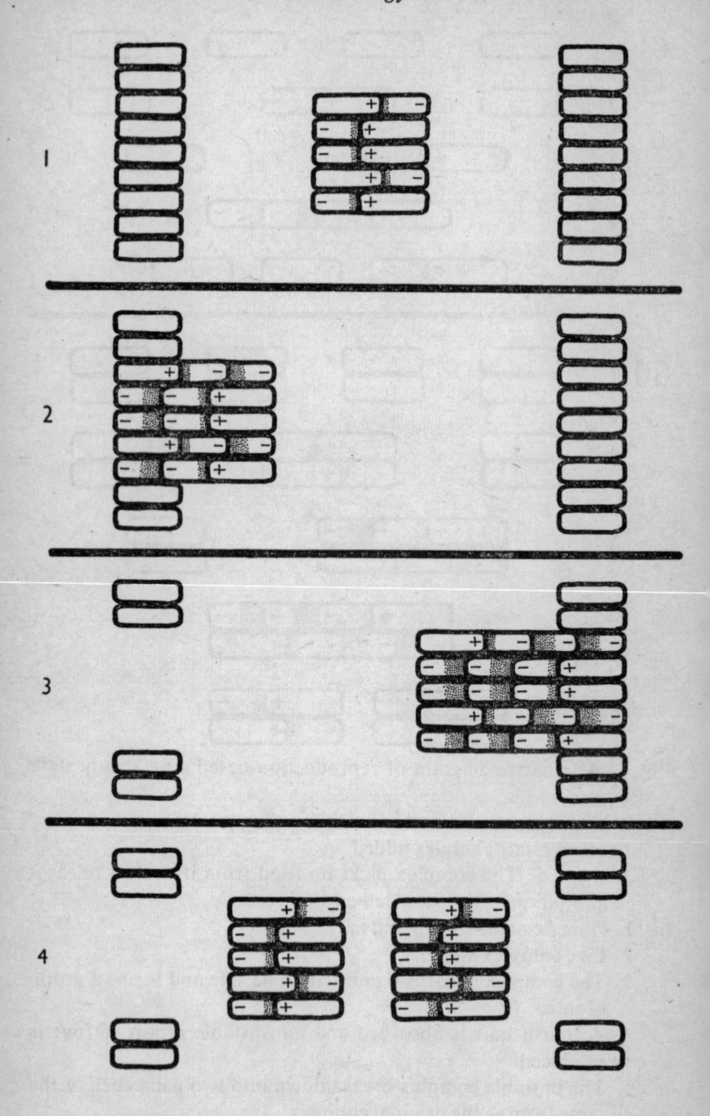
1
2
3
4

things could reproduce themselves and they may help to narrow down some biological problems by showing what can be done rather easily even if nature actually chooses a harder way. In any case there may have existed, and may still exist, organisms with methods of reproduction much simpler than that used by the nucleic acid spirals. If analogy with DNA were suggested it would mean that a dimeric unit represented a pair of nucleotides. This unit does not disintegrate in the duplication process, as DNA is believed to do, because the live complex which divides here is made up of two activated dimeric units, equivalent to two pairs of nucleotides.

It might perhaps be doubted whether the live complexes so far described are sufficiently formidable to be termed automatons in the sense envisaged by von Neumann. In order to help to meet this possible criticism, synaptons can be developed in another way. They can have basic constitutions consisting of three units, for example, instead of two. This plan led to the construction of an interesting object which has some resemblance to a cell. The two outside pieces are identical with one another in form. These represent boundary membrane and cytoplasm. They enclose a third piece which can be thought of as analogous to the nucleus.

The construction follows the same lines as that described in Fig. 6 but there are now three levels of activation instead of two. The unactivated neutral food is at zero level. The single non-reproducing complex is arranged as three elements activated in the three degrees in ascending order, 1 : 2 : 3. Feeding on the left converts the neutral element, 0, to 1, the 1 changes into 2 and the 2 to 3, all mutually linked, while the 3 stays unchanged and is repelled by the new 3. The sign : indicates a link. The sign

---

Fig. 9. Diagram of five-fold complex with arbitrary code.
The method of self-reproduction is the same as that shown in Fig. 8 (ii) 2, 3, 4, and 5, but the food material is prearranged, as in Fig. 4.

– shows the absence of a link and the presence of a repelling force. Thus,

0 . . . (1 : 2 : 3) becomes (1 : 2 : 3–3) and, eventually (1 : 2 : 3) . . . 0. The pieces, if left by themselves, drop to the lowest available energy level so that a 3 by itself drops back to zero. An exact drawing of one such mechanism is shown in Fig. 10. This pro-

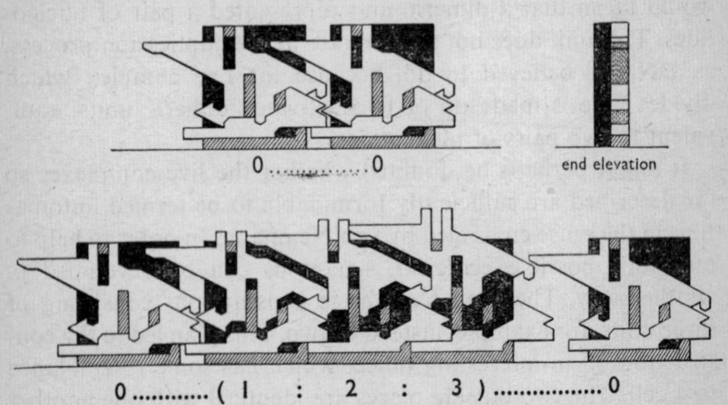

Fig. 10. Scale drawing of model in which three activated elements form a stable group.

Each element has two mobile parts; one slides vertically and does the hooking and unhooking; the other slides horizontally and carries messages.

1. Two elements in neutral phase, 0, at their lowest energy level. They do not link to one another.
2. Two elements in neutral phase, 0, on either side of an activated group (1 : 2 : 3). Close contact of the group with an element on the right would cause this element's energy level to rise, but it would not become attached. Close contact with a neutral element on the left leads to attachment there and simultaneous release of the last element at the other end.

cess of eating and excreting, which occurred as the basic structure of the model in Figs. 6, 7, and 8, is now extended to a group of three linked pieces. As before, the units can be made dimeric. A group of pieces, attached laterally but directed in the opposite sense, converts the steady metabolic process into reproduction.

As in the model described in Fig. 8, the reproducing complex feeds on units composed of pairs of neutral elements. Thus, after

```
                                      0 . . . (1 : 2 : 3)
shaking on some kind of track, stage (1), /     / / / , leads to
                                      0 . . . (3 : 2 : 1)
```

```
          (1 : 2 : 3–3)
stage (2), / / / / .
          (3–3 : 2 : 1)
```

Again, by feeding the complex in stage (2) at either end, thus,

```
0 . . . (1 : 2 : 3–3) . . . 0                          (1 : 2 : 3–3–3) . . . 0
/       / / / /         /, we arrive at stage (3), / / / / /      /.
0 . . . (3–3 : 2 : 1) . . . 0                          (3–3–3 : 2 : 1) . . . 0
```

This inflated complex still holds together in spite of the repelling forces between the 3's because of the transverse links, indicated by /, in the middle. Finally a third piece of food is absorbed and stage (4) is reached. The central pair of units is now released and two daughter complexes separate. Immediately after separation, all the elements fall to their lowest possible levels and the new complexes precisely resemble their parent. Thus,

```
           (1 : 2 : 3–3–3–3)
stage (4), / / / / / / , leads automatically to stage (5),
           (3–3–3–3 : 2 : 1)
```

```
(1 : 2 : 3) . . . (1 : 2 : 3)
 / / /            / / / . These stages are all shown diagrammati-
(3 : 2 : 1) . . . (3 : 2 : 1)
```

cally in Fig. 11.

It is natural to ask what, if anything, the study of possible modes of self-reproduction has taught us about the life processes? Some of the things we learn are really quite obvious, but often not appreciated. Many people have thought of reproduction in nature as following the pattern of printing, producing endless new copies from a templet. No doubt this is a standard method in many aspects of cell metabolism, but how does the templet replicate itself? This is the problem to which I have shown that there are several solutions. It does not seem to be necessary to form a negative to do this. The basic templet, the memory, can be self-reproducing.

The main principle involved in these mechanisms is that of the hook or ratchet. The kinetic energy of collision is turned into potential energy of structure. Every time a new complex is formed some energy is captured by the hooks; so long as food with kinetic energy is available, the potential energy of the part of the system increases. This piling up of energy is particularly

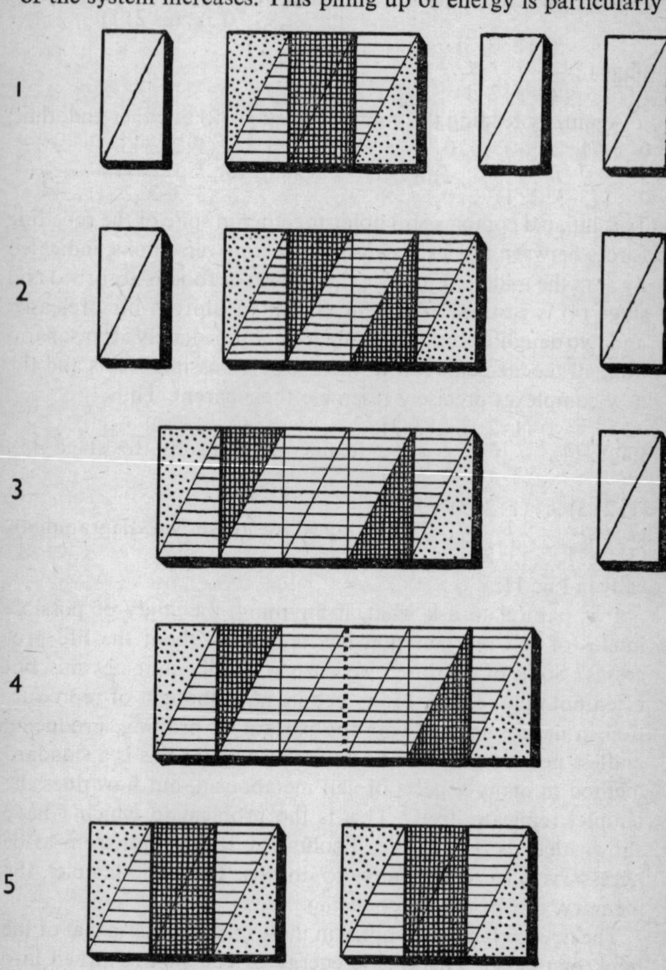

noticeable in the 'cytoplasm' of the complex shown in Fig. 11. In these parts of the complex is activation in the third degree.

In order to keep such a process going in its most elementary form, some prearrangement, in the form of strings of unprogrammed material to be used, has been found necessary. Prearrangement can be dispensed with if the code carried by the organism unlocks or selects sources of food or, indeed, assembles it. If so, the code is a necessary characteristic property of successful self-replicating systems.

I have said nothing about how a skin can be formed by use of the code which is replicated, nor have I discussed recombinations of codes from two objects with different codes. They can meet and form a third with a mixed set of instructions. This is a fundamental idea in genetics and is the origin of sexual repro-

---

Fig. 11. Reproduction of a complex composed of three units.

KEY

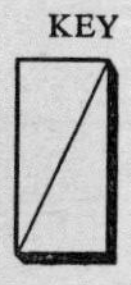

pair of elements forming a neutral unit, $\frac{0}{0}$

two elements activated in first degree (analogous to skin), 1 . . . 1

two elements activated in second degree (analogous to nuclear material), 2 . . . 2

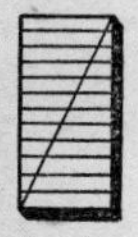

pair of elements, activated in third degree, forming a unit (analogous to cytoplasm), $\frac{3}{3}$

duction. These are problems not all easily susceptible to solution by crude mechanical models though they can be illuminated to some extent by them. A model has actually been made which has some of these properties. It is described in Fig. 12. Here a new complex can be generated by mixing the codes of two different complexes as well as by the usual methods. Such a special new complex takes half the programme of each parent, as in genetics. In Fig. 12 the crossing of two pure breeding races is demonstrated. One of them, built of two units, can reproduce itself.

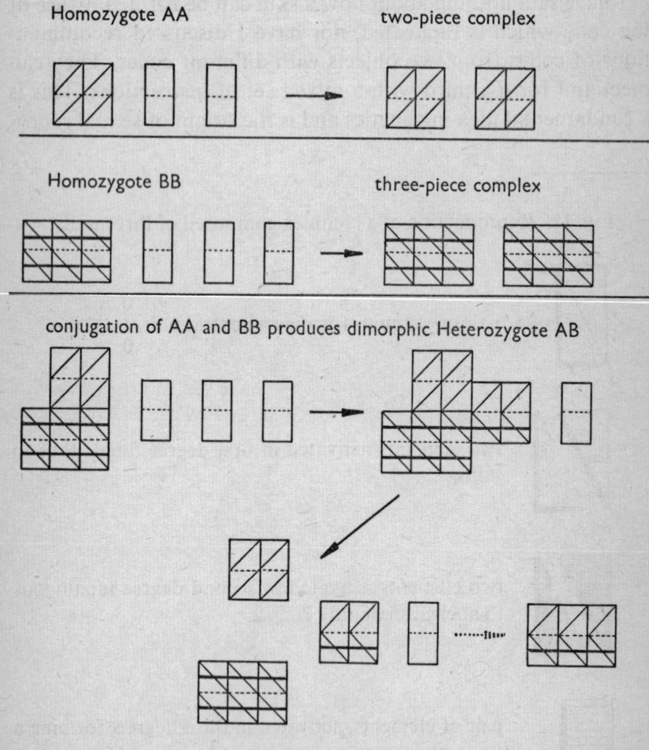

Fig. 12. Model showing two true breeding complexes, AA and BB, capable of hybridization.

Another, built of three units, can do so likewise. Conjugation of these two can lead to the formation of a hybrid. The hybrid actually produced in this experiment was asymmetrical; when fed with the same neutral material as the pure lines, it grew to a five-piece complex which broke down into two stable complexes composed of three and two units respectively. By conjugation between two hybrids the original pure line complexes could be reconstituted as in Mendelian genetics.

There are some philosophical points worth mentioning by way of a conclusion. Can a synapton be alive? The question resembles that when we ask, are viruses alive? It is a matter of definition of the properties considered to constitute a living thing. These complexes feed, grow, and reproduce. If such qualities are sufficient, they are indeed alive though, of course, they have a very low grade type of existence. It is a current way of thinking, especially among physiologists, that life is essentially connected with what are called steady states or conditions in which environmental changes are neutralized and internal equilibrium maintained. Many living organisms contain thermostatic mechanisms, for example. It may be argued, however, that these devices are not fundamental to living matter and that they do not occur in complex form in the lowest organisms. An elementary type of steady state is shown by the process of reproduction itself and this is emphasized by the metabolic flow upon which it is based.

Supposing that we concede for a moment that a synapton is alive, we can ask, further, if it is conscious? For the physiologist, the term 'conscious' applied to a rabbit bears no psychological significance but it simply means that it is neither asleep nor anaesthetized. It seems unlikely that any synapton is asleep and none has been anaesthetized so that it follows that, if alive, it must be conscious. But what about their sensations? As suggested earlier these objects share with living matter the ability to build up potential energy in the form of memory structure. In so doing, it is as though the universal enemy, the second law of thermodynamics, the law of universal scatter and decay, were cheated. A theory, which I think has some validity, is that pain is a warning of defeat in this struggle – or breakdown of structure – but that successful building is associated with pleasure. During its formation, an activated complex, if alive and conscious, may not care for the shaking process but it may be supposed to be happy at the end of the performance.

The usual method, and a very good one, of investigating the nature of living things is to observe them, dissect, extract, and dissolve them in various ways to see what they are made of and how they work. The new method proposed in this lecture has not been much tried but possibly it will also prove fruitful. That is, while investigating von Neumann's problem, we construct objects with properties like living things. We can then examine them carefully, observing their abilities and limitations, and study their natural history.

But there is nothing quite new in the world. Epicurus held that the juxtaposition of atoms in empty space could lead to the formation of living beings. Let me finish by quoting Lucretius, who wrote more than 1,000 years ago:

'Driven along in an incessant but variable movement some [atoms] bounce far apart after a collision while others recoil only a short distance from the impact . . . those that do not recoil far being driven into a closer union and held there by the entanglement of their own interlocking shapes. . . . It must not be supposed that atoms of every sort can be linked in every variety of combination. If that were so, you would see monsters coming into being everywhere. . . We see that everything is created from specific seeds, born of a specific mother and grows up true to type.'

REFERENCES

Haldane, J. B. S. 1954. 'The origin of life.' *New Biology*, **16**, 12

Latham, R. (trs.) 1951. *Lucretius on the nature of the universe.* Harmondsworth, Penguin Books.

von Neumann, J. 1951. *Cerebral mechanisms in behaviour.* New York and London, McGraw Hill.

Oparin, A. I. 1957. *The origin of life on earth.* 3rd Edn. Trs. Ann Synge. Edinburgh, Oliver and Boyd.

Penrose, L. S., and Penrose, R. 1957. 'A self-reproducing analogue.' *Nature,* **179**, 1183.

Schrödinger, E. 1944. *What is life?* Cambridge University Press.

Further developments of this work are discussed in:

Penrose, L. S. 1958. 'Mechanics of self-reproduction.' *Ann. Genet., London,* **23**, 59.

A 16-mm. sound film on the subject of the article is obtainable through Mr H. A. Cresswell, 22 Longlands, Hemel Hempstead, Hertfordshire.

HAIR

N. A. BARNICOT

Illustrations between pp. 68 and 69

AMONG the many kinds of spines, filaments, and spikes that adorn the surfaces of animals and plants, mammalian hair is a distinct and characteristic structure. Nothing truly comparable is to be found in living reptiles and the feathers of birds which are developed in a similar way and are composed of essentially the same horny material, are easily distinguished from it.

We know next to nothing about the stages in the evolution of hair, since it is not preserved in fossils from the more remote periods when the mammal-like reptiles or the earliest mammalian forms were living. It has been suggested, however, that certain markings on the snout bones of one of the former group may have been due to the presence of whiskers. An examination of living mammals does not help very much, since even in those which are in other respects most primitive, nothing is found which can be regarded as a transitional stage to hair.

From a consideration of living mammals in general we can infer that the ancestral forms possessed a fairly uniform hair covering with the hairs sloping backwards from head to tail leaving only a few areas naked, such as the skin round the nostrils and the palms of the hands and soles of the feet.

The general functions of hair

Perhaps the most fundamental function of hair and the one of prime significance in mammalian evolution is that of insulation. Broadly speaking, mammals maintain a body temperature of 37–40° C even when the surrounding air is much cooler; it is true that there are various grades in the efficiency of this temperature regulation and that some forms (resting bats and hibernating species, for example) may on occasion allow their body temperature to fall much lower in cool surroundings, but the generalization is valid that the activity of mammals is less dependent on external temperature than that of reptiles, which can move only sluggishly in cold surroundings. The prevention of heat loss, due to the layer of air trapped among the hairs, is an important factor in heat regulation. The same principle is, of course, used by man, with his inadequate hairy covering, when he dresses in skins or woven fibres, and is dramatically illustrated by the device of the string vest worn below other garments.

Animals which are hairless are at a disadvantage in cold climates particularly if they are small and therefore present a relatively large surface for heat loss. Those which are born hairless are protected in a nest or pouch of some kind until the hair develops. In view of the importance of hair as an isulator it may seem surprising at first sight that it is much reduced in some aquatic forms such as whales, since water carries away heat rapidly; but the loss is compensated in those animals by the thick layer of fat below the skin and the naked surface is presumably more efficient from the point of view of frictional resistance. It may be significant that the early mammals, which were small, were also probably nocturnal, as many species still are. In many parts of the world the nights are cold although the days are hot, and it is possible that superior heat regulation may have given mammals a particular advantage as active hunters by night, when many reptiles were immobilized.

A second important function of hair is that of a tactile organ. The hairs act as levers, slight movements of which stimulate nerve endings around their roots. Specially long hairs on the snout and in tufts near the eye and on the lower jaw are found in many mammals, and in nocturnal forms may be more useful than the eyes. The eyelashes cause very rapid reflex shutting of the eyelid when a speck of dust hits them.

Thirdly the pigments of the hair are mainly responsible for the diversity of colour and pattern which help in avoiding enemies and in attracting the other sex or other members of the herd. Variation in the length and direction of the hairs may also play a part in accentuating the pattern.

Some modifications of hair

The evolution of a major group of animals usually provides examples of extreme divergence of structure from the general type, often in a way which is clearly related to some peculiar way of life. The quills of porcupines and hedgehogs are single hairs enlarged for the purpose of defence and transitions to ordinary hair are easy to see on the body of animal. We find the same thing again in the spiny ant-eater (Proechidna) of Australasia, a representative of the small group of monotreme animals. Porcupines, hedgehogs, and monotremes belong to different mammalian groups which are only remotely related, so that the modification of hairs as quills has certainly taken place independently in each of them.

Reduction of hair has occurred in members of several different mammalian groups and hairless forms of domestic and laboratory stocks occasionally turn up as genetical mutations. The whales have already been mentioned and the sea-cows are another case in point. Seals and sea-lions have fur, but the hairs of the over-fur have a peculiar flattened shape. In the armadillos some hair remains between the hard scales, which are formed from bone produced in the dermis and covered by a layer of horn produced by the epidermis. The remarkable overlapping scales of the pangolins are not, as some have supposed, made of consolidated hairs but are also a development of the horny surface layer of the epidermis and a few hairs occur on the softer skin between them. The elephants, rhinoceroses and hippopotamuses are examples of warm climate animals of large size which show considerable reduction of the hair covering, though hairy species of the two former lived in the Ice Age as we know from actual specimens preserved in the tundra, as well as from cave paintings.

The reduction of hair in man as compared with other Primates is obvious enough, but we must consider more carefully at this point what we actually mean by hairiness. The superficial impression of hairiness depends not only on the number of hairs per unit area but also on the length, thickness, and colour of the hair, and some areas of the human body which appear at first sight to be hairless in fact produce very fine colourless hairs. Counting the number of hairs on an area of skin of standard size is one of the ways which has been used to get an exact comparison of hairiness. Dr Szabo at the London Hospital has done this for various regions of the human body, using a special technique in which the epidermal layer is removed as a continuous sheet so that the hair follicles, which are the structures which form the hairs, can be seen attached to the lower surface. Comparisons of man with apes and monkeys have been undertaken by counting hairs on specimens of preserved skin. A. H. Schultz, who was at that time at the Johns Hopkins medical school, found nearly 2,000 hairs per square centimetre on the scalp and back of a New World monkey and about the same number in a gibbon, but only 300 or so in the chimpanzee and orang. The hair density on the human scalp equalled or surpassed that in apes, but very few hairs were found on the back. In all these Primates the hair density on the chest was considerably lower than on the other two regions, though in the human male those hairs that do occur may be long and conspicuous.

Growth and development of hair

The first rudiments of hair appear early in foetal life: in the human foetus they can be found on the face region between the second and third months of gestation. The hairs are formed by a downgrowth of cells from the superficial (epidermal) layer of the skin into the connective tissue layer (dermis) below it. The tips of these epidermal pegs become bell shaped and the hollow of the bell surrounds a distinctive mass of dermal cells known as the dermal papilla. The whole structure formed in this way from epidermis and dermis is the hair follicle, a diagram of which is shown in the text figure. There is reason to think that the dermal papilla plays an essential part in formation and re-generation of hair though its cells are not actually incorporated in the hair shaft; it is probable that the downgrowth and differentiation of the epidermal bud is due to some stimulus from the underlying dermal cells.

The hair covering of many mammals consists of two or more fairly distinct types of hair; firstly the long, coarse guard hairs comprising the over-fur which contributes most to the surface appearance and secondly, shorter, finer hairs which are hidden by the guard hairs and may include more than one structural type. In specialized wool-producing breeds of sheep the coat consists very largely of long under-fur; a few coarse guard hairs (kemp) can be found in the adult sheep but are more numerous in the new-born animal. Although human hair varies greatly in length and thickness in different parts of the body, an almost continuous gradation can be found and distinct types cannot be distinguished.

Human beings also differ from many mammals in having no well-defined periods of shedding and replacement of hair. In some animals there is an annual moult at a definite season while in others, such as the rat and mouse, there are more or less regular cycles of hair moult and regeneration at shorter intervals. New hairs are formed in the follicles from which the old hairs are shed; the follicles themselves appear early in foetal life and probably few if any new ones are formed in the older animal. The regeneration of hair after a moult may start at certain definite points and spread from there over the whole body as in the rat, or it may occur in a random manner all over the skin. During intra-uterine life man is covered with a rather uniform coat of fine hair, known as lanugo; this hair extends over the scalp and on to the forehead without interruption. Lanugo is shed before birth or soon after and the scalp hair becomes differentiated from the much finer hair on the forehead. In a new-born child the hair follicles situated in a unit area of skin are more numerous than in the adult, but as the area of the skin increases they become more widely spaced.

Follicles which at first formed only fine hairs may later produce much larger ones. This is conspicuously true at puberty when coarse hair begins to be formed in the arm-pit, pubic region and in the beard area of males. The growth of coarse hair on the arms, legs, chest, shoulders and on the line between the navel and pubis continues slowly in adult life in the male, but varies in degree in different individuals. These changes in the activity of particular hair follicles depend on the secretion of certain hormones which will be discussed more fully later.

The changes at puberty which stimulate some follicles to form larger hairs may have a very different effect on others, which may respond by shedding hair and thereafter producing only very fine ones; in human males for example there is a certain amount of recession of the hair-line on the forehead and temples and this may continue in adult life until the long, coarse type of hair only remains at the sides of the head. This pattern-baldness apparently depends on the hormonal secretion of the testis, since it does not occur in eunuchs castrated before puberty, but it also depends on the genetic constitution of the individual, since not all men are bald and the condition tends to run in families.

Baldness of this type seems to be less common in Mongoloid peoples and also in negroes, though it must be admitted that our knowledge is mainly based on casual observation rather than exact data. Hamilton, an American worker, has investigated the amount of beard and axillary (arm-pit) hair in white Americans and in Japanese. He used the total weight of hair as a measure and showed that in both groups the beard reached a maximum development at about 25–30 years of age, thereafter remaining constant until old age. Axillary hair reached a maximum at 30 years and then decreased steadily in amount due to the production of fewer and thinner hairs. The Japanese at all ages after puberty had on average only one-half to one-third of the amount in the American subjects. The popular belief that abundant hairiness is a sign of great sexual potency seems to have no scientific foundation, at least as far as the normal population is concerned, and may well be founded on the recognition of pubertal changes and the scant hair development of eunuchs. It is probable that differences in hairiness between both individuals and racial groups are due mainly to intrinsic properties of the hair follicle which are determined in some unknown manner by genetic constitution.

The structure of the hair follicle

If the reader cares to pluck a few hairs from his head he will probably find that some of them have about two millimetres of soft, whitish tissue at the root end while others have only a much smaller blob of tissue confined to the extreme tip. These two types of plucked follicle are illustrated in Plate 1*a* and 1*b*. The former are the more actively growing hairs and the tissue which comes away in plucking consists of cells which would ultimately have been converted into the substance of the mature hair or into certain sheaths which surround the forming shaft below the skin (see text figure).

The structure and activities of the hair follicle have been rather intensively studied in recent years because interference with hair growth is an early and sensitive sign of damage due to radiation from atomic explosions. The subject is also interesting to those concerned in trying to find cures for baldness, to workers engaged in studying the growth of wool and to medical men who deal with diseases of the endocrine glands.

It may be easiest to deal first with the architecture of mature hair. A mature hair is not a homogenous structure; the surface is covered by a layer of overlapping scales, known as the cuticle, and the shape and arrangement of these scales, each of which represents a single cell, varies somewhat in different animals. The hair of bats, which is very fine, has scales with slender points projecting from their edges (Plate 2*b*). In the hair of sloths (Plate 2*a*) unicellular green algae, similar to those on the bark of trees, are found embedded in the loose textured surface layer.

Certain components of the hair cuticle are remarkably resistant to chemical attack. The cuticle forms a barrier to the penetration of dyestuffs and the projecting edge of the scales also gives the hair greater frictional resistance when dragged from root to tip than in the opposite direction. Both these properties are important in the industrial processing of wool so that a good deal of work on the cuticle has been done in the research laboratories of the wool industry.

The bulk of the hair, lying within the cuticle, is called the cor-

A diagram (not to scale) of a growing hair follicle. A segment has been cut out to show the internal structure, and the mature hair shaft with sheaths removed is shown in the top portion.

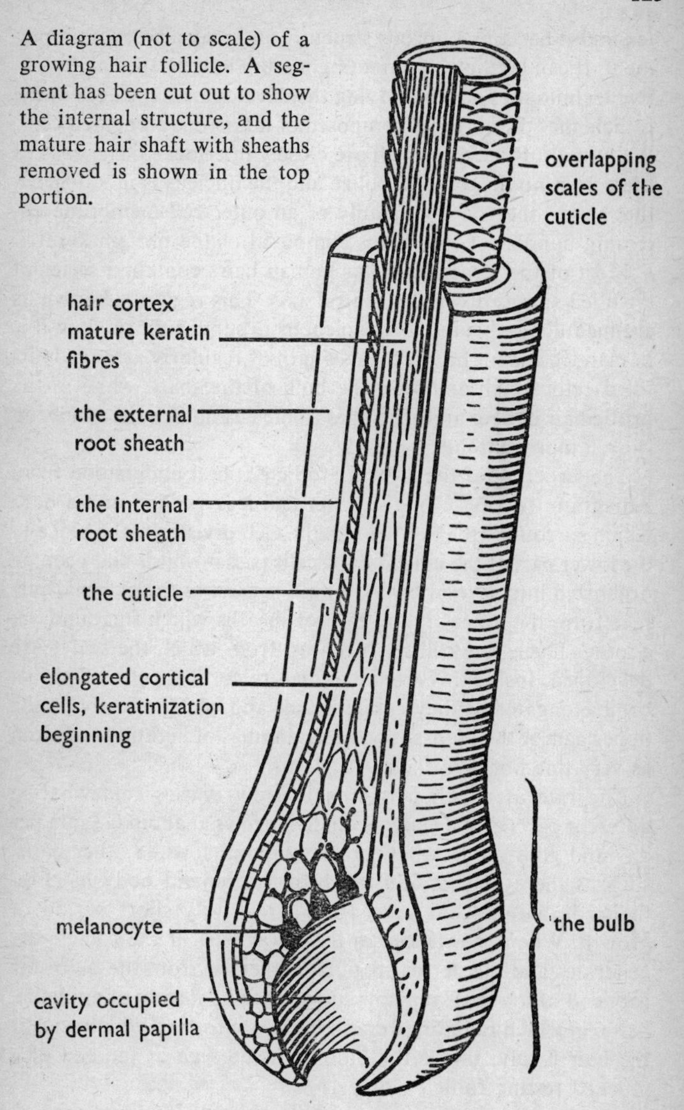

tex and it has a fine fibrous structure and may also contain pigment. It can be shown by treating mature hair by special disruptive techniques and by studying the developmental stages in the follicle that the cortex is composed of numerous elongated cells, the fluted surfaces of which are closely interlocked The cells of the cortex no longer metabolize and the nucleus is in a degenerate state: they consist mainly of an outer cell membrane enclosing bundles of fine fibres composed of the protein keratin.

Most of the larger diameter human hairs contain a series of air-filled spaces down the central axis. This region is known as the medulla and is more conspicuous in some animals than it is in man; in rodent hair it forms a pith of regularly arranged air-filled cells which comprise the bulk of the shaft, while in the brittle hair of deer and antelopes (Plate 2*c* and 2*d*) this condition is even more extreme.

The structure of the growing follicle is best understood from a diagram (text fig.). At the lower end it is swollen into a bulb which surrounds the dermal papilla. Cell divisions take place in the lower part of the bulb and the cells pass upwards and become organized into several layers. Those nearest to the external surface form the inner and outer root sheaths which surround yet another layer, one cell in thickness, from which the scales are developed. Inside this are the immature cortical cells which become elongated as they pass upwards and which already, in the upper part of the bulb, show the beginnings of keratin formation as very fine fibrils in their cytoplasm.

The rate at which human hair grows varies somewhat in different parts of the body. Scalp hair grows at about 0·3 mm per day and goes on growing for many months, while other hairs, such as the eyelashes and much of the general body hair, remains in a quiescent state after a relatively short period of growth. When growth ceases the lower part of the follicle degenerates and the dermal papilla is released from the bulb; the root end of the shaft remains surrounded by a mass of epithelial tissue in which radiating keratin fibres are formed which anchor the hair firmly; this is the blob of tissue seen at the end of a plucked resting follicle (Plate 1*b*).

The factors which control the regular cycle of hair growth in animals like the rat are by no means fully known. Experimental work indicates that thyroxin, the hormone of the thyroid gland, stimulates new growth in the follicles, while cortisone, a substance closely related to some of the hormones of the adrenal gland, suppresses it. Hair growth cycles are also suppressed if the pituitary gland is removed, but this may be because other endocrine glands are themselves functionally dependent on the hormones produced by the pituitary.

When growth of a resting follicle is resumed, cells from the external root sheath extend downwards into the lower layers of the dermis and again form a bulb which encloses a dermal papilla; formation of a new hair in the manner already described then starts, and the old hair shaft falls out, making way for the emergence of a new one. Resumption of active growth in resting follicles can be initiated by a wide variety of different stimuli such as mechanical or chemical irritation and this fact has caused much confusion in the search for specific hair-growth stimulants.

Keratin

Keratin, the fibrous horny material of hair, has perhaps been studied more than any other protein because of its importance in the wool industry, but much still remains to be learned about its detailed structure. One of the difficulties is that it is a hard, relatively insoluble protein, the molecules of which are firmly bonded together and hard to separate without causing changes in the original structure. Like other proteins it is composed of numerous different amino-acids and it is one of the large group of fibrous proteins in which the amino-acids are combined to form long, chain-like molecules. In comparison with many other proteins it has a high content of the amino-acid cystine which contains sulphur. It is clear that much of the mechanical strength and insolubility of keratin is due to bonds between the sulphur-containing groups of this cystine component. When these disulphide bonds as they are called are broken by alkali or by various other chemical treatments, among which the action of peracetic acid is perhaps the most specific, the keratin molecules fall apart much more easily so that the strength of the fibres is greatly reduced. Although it is mainly composed of keratin, hair is not a homogeneous material, such as a chemist might prefer to deal with, but contains small amounts of other substances, and some workers think that even the keratin fibres themselves may not be a single compound, but a composite structure containing more than one protein fraction. The chemical complexity of hair and wool is perhaps not surprising in view of their complicated development by the transformation of various cells.

The technique of X-ray diffraction, which is widely used for revealing the arrangement of atoms in crystalline material, was applied to the study of keratin at an early date and has contributed greatly to our understanding of its structure. The molecular chains are normally folded in a regular manner, but become straightened out when a hair is stretched. The fact that a hair can be stretched to some 30 per cent of its initial length if it is immersed in water, and will return to its original state if released and allowed to rest, is the basis of mechanical tests of hair elasticity which are used in wool research to detect chemical damage to the fibres.

Recently radioactive isotopes have been used to determine the point of entry of cystine into the hair follicle. Cystine containing radioactive sulphur was given to the animals and the hair follicles were then removed and prepared as thin sections. When sections were placed in contact with a photographic plate the regions containing the radioactive material could be detected by their local effect on the emulsion. Injected cystine enters the growing follicle in a matter of minutes mainly in the region just above the bulb, where keratinization is very active and where a rich plexus of fine blood vessels surrounds the follicle.

A variant of hair form which turns up naturally in many species, including man, is the waved or spiralized type. In the highly crimped hairs of merino wool it can be shown by the reaction to dyestuffs and to various forms of chemical attack that the keratin on the two sides of the curvature is different. The more resistant form is found on the concave side and is the first to be laid down in development. The follicle of crimped wool is markedly curved and this is also the case in negro scalp follicles; nevertheless tests which show up the bilateral differences in wool keratin are inconclusive when applied to human hair. The shape of the follicle presumably imposes a curvature on the hair shaft before it is fully hardened; in sheep suffering from copper deficiency and also in negro children suffering from a nutritional disease known as kwashiokor, keratinization of the hair shaft is delayed and the curvature of the emerging shaft is less pronounced.

Hair pigments

The hair colour of mammals has a fairly restricted range, varying from black to white and through various shades of grey, brown, yellow, and red. Very often single hairs are not uniformly coloured but have well-defined bands of different colour along their length; in man there may be slight gradations of colour along the shaft of individual hairs, but definite pigmentary banding does not occur.

It is easy to see under the microscope, at least in the case of the darker colours, that the pigment is present in the form of very small granules. The structure of these granules can be made out much more clearly under the electron microscope (Plate 1*c*) since their length is only 1/1000th of a millimetre or less, which approaches the limits for clear perception of detail under the light microscope.

The pigment granules of both skin and hair are produced by special cells called melanocytes. These are not formed by the differentiation of epidermal cells, but they migrate into the skin at an early stage of embryonic development from a region adjacent to the rudiment of the central nervous system (neural crest). In the skin they are situated in the layer of the epidermis nearest to the dermis while in the hair follicle (text fig.) they lie in the epidermal part of the bulb adjacent to the upper region of the dermal papilla. Their form is quite distinct from the epithelial cells of the skin or hair bulb: they have fine branches extending from the cell body and terminating in bulb-like endings on the epidermal cells of the skin or the immature cortical cells of the hair. Electron microscopy has made it possible to see the stages in the formation of the pigment granules; they develop from small vacuoles in a special area of the melanocyte and pass along the processes and finally into the epidermal cells or the cortical cells of the hair as the case may be. The melanocytes are particularly sensitive to X-rays and after irradiation of the skin with suitable doses, most of them are killed so that the hairs which ultimately regenerate from the damaged follicles are white.

The hair and skin pigments belong to a group of compounds known as melanins which are widely distributed in both plants and animals; the black spores of some fungi and the ink of cuttle-fish are good examples. These pigments are formed by the oxidation of phenolic substances to quinones which readily combine to form dark, highly insoluble compounds. The structure of the final pigments is very difficult to determine, but there is good evidence that the mammalian melanins, and probably many others, are formed from the amino-acid tyrosine. The initial stages in the oxidation of tyrosine in the melanocytes are controlled by an enzyme, tyrosinase, which has been isolated from certain melanin-producing tumours. The pigment in the melanin granules is combined with protein; the formation of a dark and hard melanoprotein by the combination of protein with the oxidation products of a phenol also occurs in the formation of the resistant cuticle of many insects. In the case of albinism, an inherited condition in which melanin formation is absent or very much reduced in amount, tyrosinase activity cannot be demonstrated although abortive melanin granules can be seen in the melanocytes.

Because variations in hair colour can be so easily observed they have played a large part in mammalian genetics. Working on laboratory animals it has been possible to pin-point many of the genes which affect the colour or the distribution of the pigment, but the difficulties which the melanins present to the chemist have proved an obstacle to more fundamental analysis in biochemical terms. Genetical work on pigmentary variation in man is also fraught with difficulties that can be overcome in animal experiments. Family material has to be analysed as it occurs, without the advantages of controlled breeding experiments. As far as our knowledge goes at present there is no reason to doubt that the more or less continuous gradations of pigmentation which are found in human populations are due to the small cumulative effects of many genes. The pronounced changes of hair colour with age add to the difficulties of family studies on the genetics of human hair colour. Red hair is sometimes cited as an example of inheritance due to a single recessive gene, but this is certainly an over-simplification. One trouble is that red hair is not a sharply defined character but grades into brown and blonde colours. In recent years the use of photoelectric instruments which record the amount of light reflected from the hair or skin throughout the spectrum have made a more accurate characterization of pigmentation possible. Accurate quantitative measurements are always to be preferred to rough visual judgements, both in studying families and also in surveying the distribution of pigmentation in different parts of the world.

Hair and endocrinology

Changes in hair growth may provide the clinician with useful diagnostic signs of certain disturbances of the endocrine glands, and conversely, the study of such cases provides information about the physiological control of hair growth in man. Animal experiments may also give useful indications, but must be interpreted with caution because the responses of an animal such as the rat, with its cycles of hair change, may well be different from those of the human subject in some respects.

Some tumours of the pituitary gland secrete abnormally large amounts of a hormone, adrenocorticotrophin, known as ACTH for short, which is required for the normal maintenance and function of the adrenal cortex. Among the secretions of the adrenal cortex are compounds which have a masculinizing effect (androgens) like the hormones of the reproductive glands. This disorder of the pituitary therefore results in the excessive production of androgens by the adrenal cortex which stimulate hair growth in the beard area, and also on the body, in females. Other serious abnormalities occur in these diseases, but hirsutism in female patients is a particularly distressing result. In other cases the hirsute condition is due to a tumour of the adrenal cortex itself; these tumours may simply secrete larger amounts of the usual adrenocortical hormones but there are some types in which there is a deviation in the synthetic activities of tumour tissue and their hormone production is not only increased in amount but abnormal in composition. One form of this last type has an onset before birth resulting in precocious puberty. It must not be thought that all cases of hirsutism in females are due to these severe glandular disturbances, which are fortunately rare; in many instances no definite evidence of hormonal abnormalities can be detected.

A good deal remains to be learned about the part played by the endocrine glands in the events of normal puberty. Certain pituitary hormones (gonadotrophins) stimulate growth of the ovary and testis which themselves begin to produce large amounts of oestrogenic hormones in the female and of the androgen, testosterone, in the male. Growth of the pubic, axillary, and beard hair in the male is stimulated by the testicular hormone and this hair therefore remains juvenile in castrates; some growth of the axillary hair can be produced by applying the hormone locally to the skin in oily solution. The growth of the pubic and axillary hair in females is probably brought about by the increased secretion of androgenic hormones by the adrenal cortex at puberty. The possibilities of mutual interaction between the various glands, together with differing sensitivities of the hair follicles in different regions, make it difficult to piece together a coherent and satisfactory picture. There has been much work on the excretion of the gonadal, adrenal, and pituitary hormones in the urine, in which they often appear as derivatives rather than in their original form, and in some cases quantitative estimates can be made of the hormones in the circulating blood; at present, however, most of the methods are laborious and require a good deal of skill. Careful and prolonged observations on children over the course of puberty, correlating the anatomical changes with biochemical measures of endocrine activity will no doubt add much to our knowledge in the future.

REFERENCES

Montagna, W., and Ellis, R. A. ed. 1958. *The Biology of Hair Growth.* New York, Academic Press.

Rothman, S. 1954. *Physiology and Biochemistry of the Skin.* Chicago University Press.

Montagna, W. 1956. *The Structure and Function of Skin.* New York, Academic Press.

SOME RECENT BIOLOGICAL BOOKS

A Handbook on Evolution by Gavin de Beer (London, British Museum (Natural History)), 110 pp. 5s. An extensive essay on the theory of evolution introduces a description of each of the fifteen exhibits which have been prepared to commemorate the centenary of the Darwin-Wallace publication. A beautiful example of verbal and visual exposition of some fundamentals of biology.

Our Plate 3 shows the case illustrating Geographical variation. The deermouse provides an example of a colour cline; on the West coast of U.S.A. it is dark brown, and passing eastwards becomes grey then paler and more orange, grey again, and then darker and browner in the Eastern forests. The gulls give an example of a 'ring' species. In Great Britain the lesser black-backed gull and the herring gull behave as separate species, but they are the two ends of a circumpolar ring of interbreeding varieties. The puffin is an example of a size cline, with large birds in the north, smaller in the south.

The Kew Series: British Wild Flowers by Patricia Lewis, 376 pp., 15 colour plates and 170 line drawings, 25s.: *British Trees and Shrubs* by R. D. Meikle, 244 pp., 15 colour plates and 84 line drawings, 25s (London, Eyre and Spottiswoode, 1958). With so many books on British plants available, new ones must expect a cool reception. Yet these two volumes, the first to appear of a series of five, have the authority of Kew behind them and are intended to fill the gap which exists between popular accounts and the somewhat forbidding floras of the specialist. This they do rather well: the format and illustrations are especially attractive, scientific accuracy has been retained, and a great deal of information about distribution, habitat, nomenclature, uses and biological peculiarities is included. This has not been achieved without sacrifice and many species, including all the sedges and grasses, have been left undescribed. However, these books will provide the student with a sound introduction to the British flora and its classification and encourage him to use the more advanced and complete works.

A Century of Darwin. Edited by S. A. Barnett (London, Heinemann, 1958), 376 pp., 30s. This is the outstanding book of those which have celebrated the centenary of the first announcement of evolution by natural selection. It contains 15 contributions, some by biologists with great reputations, others, just as valuable, by members of the younger generation. Darwin's many different but interwoven interests in biology are looked at from the standpoint of today's knowledge, so that the book is both a tribute to Darwin's superb range of contributions to science and an admirable survey of many current biological ideas.

The Biological Replication of Macromolecules. Symposium of the Society for Experimental Biology Number XII. (Cambridge University Press, 1958), 255 pp., 50s. The Symposia of the S.E.B. are scientific summit meetings of international biologists, and the papers presented are naturally highly technical in language though often highly exciting in content. We draw attention to the most recent volume because it is concerned with the reproduction of complex structure, a field into which Professor Penrose has made such a startlingly original incursion in the present number of *New Biology.* Living things are commonly defined by the power of self-reproduction. In this sense the artificial synthesis of living systems from less unconventional raw material than the plywood used by Penrose may not be so far off, and the raw knowledge is to be found in this volume.

ABOUT OUR CONTRIBUTORS

P. D. F. MURRAY has been Profesor of Zoology in the University of Sydney since 1949. He trained at Sydney and Oxford, and spent twenty years in England in research and university teaching. His main work has been on skeletal development; he is the author of a book on the subject, *Bones* (1936).

A. G. N. FLEW, M.A. (Oxon.), is Professor of Philosophy, University College of North Staffordshire. Publications include: *Logic and Language* (Editor: first series, 1951. Second series 1953); *A New Approach to Psychical Research* (1953); *New Essays in Philosophical Theology* (Joint Editor with A. MacIntyre, 1955); *Essays in Conceptual Analysis* (Editor, 1956); and numerous articles in the philosophers' trade journals and elsewhere.

A. B. ACTON is a lecturer in the Department of Zoology of the University College of N. Wales, Bangor. He graduated at Oxford University and worked for two years in the Department of Genetics at Glasgow. He is particularly interested in the giant chromosomes of the midge *Chironomus*.

J. HESLOP HARRISON is Professor of Botany in the Queen's University of Belfast, and was formerly Reader in Botany at University College London. His research interests lie in the fields of genecology and experimental morphology.

L. S. PENROSE is Galton Professor of Eugenics at University College London. His best known research has been on mental defect, particularly on its genetic aspects, and he is author of *The Biology of Mental Defect* (1949). He is a Fellow of the Royal Society.

N. A. BARNICOT was formerly a Zoologist at University College London and is at present Reader in Physical Anthropology there. In recent years he has published work on various aspects of human pigmentation including electron microscope studies on the structure and formation of hair pigments, and survey work on skin and hair colour variation using reflectance techniques.